MORE THAN
BLUES

MORE THAN JUST THE
BLUES

UNDERSTANDING SERIOUS
TEENAGE PROBLEMS

Dr JOSEPH REY

SIMON & SCHUSTER

AUSTRALIA

First published as *Is My Teenager in Trouble?* in Australia in 1995
by Simon & Schuster (Australia) Pty Limited
20 Barcoo Street, East Roseville NSW 2069

A Viacom Company
Sydney New York London

This edition
MORE THAN JUST THE BLUES
First published in 2002

National Library of Australia
Cataloguing-in-Publication data

Rey, Joseph
    More than just the blues: understanding serious teenage problems.

    2nd ed.
    Includes index.
    ISBN 0 7318 0776 6.

    1. Teenagers. 2. Adolescent psychology. 3. Parent and
    teenager. I. Title

    649.125

Cover design by Gayna Murphy, Greendot Design
Text design and typesetting by Patricia Ansell
Printed in Australia by Griffin Press

10 9 8 7 6 5 4 3 2 1

Contents

Acknowledgments

*Many people contributed to this book in one way or another.
My thanks to:*

The teenagers I have treated over the years and their families.

The parent who suggested that I write the book and made it possible.

Jean Starling who helped with the chapter on eating disorders.

Thomas and Eileen Merrick and Margaret Davis for their suggestions.

All the staff at Rivendell, particularly Ross Black, Jon Plapp, Garry Walter and Chris Wever.

Jennifer Fergus, Anne Gripton and Christine Knowles, several school counsellors who did not wish to be named, and child and adolescent mental health staff from Northern Sydney Health. They made very useful suggestions for the second edition.

Introduction

People believed for many years that adolescence was a stage of development in which erratic, emotional and irrational behaviour was the norm rather than the exception. They saw it as time of storm and stress, so much so that some said it was abnormal for a teenager not to be troubled.

The word 'adolescent' still brings to mind the picture of a rebellious, moody, opinionated, noisy and unpleasant individual, neither a child nor an adult. Many parents who thoroughly enjoy seeing their small children grow up dread their becoming teenagers. There is always at hand some story – a relative who wasted her future, a friend's son who became a drug addict or a neighbour who was a failure – to make parents conscious of the dangers of adolescence, let alone sensational media reports of crime and mayhem. The result is that parents often worry too much. However, worried parents are tense, insecure parents and this is not a good indicator for a harmonious, stable and enjoyable family life.

The image of every teenager as troubled cannot be further from the truth. The vast majority of adolescents are caring, intelligent, idealistic and stable people who love and appreciate their families and their country.

Nevertheless, some teenagers do have serious problems. This book deals specifically with them: how to know if a problem is serious, what the causes are and which treatments are available. Knowing what to look for and understanding what can be done about it are important tools that will make you more effective in helping and seeking help for your child.

This book was written with parents in mind. However, other people who have regular contact with adolescents or families, such as school counsellors, teachers, general practitioners, direct care workers, ministers of religion, to name a few, may find reading it valuable. Adolescents who suffer from any of the conditions described here may also find reading the specific chapter helpful.

I use throughout the book the words 'psychological disorder', 'psychiatric disorder' and 'mental disorder' interchangeably to mean a serious mental health problem. 'Disorder', 'illness', 'syndrome' and 'condition' are also used interchangeably.

Chapters 1–5 give general background about adolescence and how to handle normal teenage behaviour. This part also describes how to distinguish what is within the range of normality and what is abnormal, what are the causes of mental health problems, how to go about seeking help and what can be expected in the way of treatment. The remainder of the book focuses on specific problems, such as depression or anxiety. The case studies sprinkled throughout the book are fictional, although they reflect the kind of situations found in real life.

The information provided reflects current opinion, what is known or accepted by most experts at the time of publication. Readers ought to keep in mind that this is a very condensed guide that applies to general situations and is not a substitute for professional help. I hope you will find the book useful.

Adolescence 1

T his chapter describes what adolescence is and some of the changes that take place during this stage of development. You probably know most of this information, but it is useful to repeat it because it will help you to understand issues in later chapters of the book.

What is adolescence?

Adolescence is the stage of development that bridges the gap between childhood and adult life. The changes that take place during this period transform individuals who are physically and emotionally dependent for survival on parents or family into independent persons, able to take care of themselves and ready to establish and nurture a new family. That is, they become full members of the community and can make a contribution to it.

The marked physical changes – for example, the growth spurt, the breaking of the voice, the development of facial hair in boys and of breasts in girls – are but an indication of the metamorphosis that goes on inside.

Understanding this transformation, and the struggle teenagers go through in coming to terms with the huge changes that this entails, will go a long way towards helping you make sense of your teenage child's behaviour.

When does adolescence start and when does it end?

Adolescence starts with puberty, when the child has become functionally able to procreate offspring. This is marked in girls by the beginning of periods but is less clear cut in boys. Puberty does not occur at the same time in all children. Most Western societies are organised to cope with adolescence starting at about the age of 12 years. This coincides with the beginning of secondary school.

> *The increasing need for knowledge and skills has a direct impact on the psychological and social aspects of growing up.*

The end of adolescence is vague. It merges gradually with adulthood and varies a lot from person to person. Although many people think that adult life starts after the end of the teenage years, this is not necessarily so. The demands of modern life, which require more training and learning of skills, keep many people dependent on their parents into their twenties. Joan, for example, was completely independent by the age of 18 years. Although short of money, she managed to rent a flat with a girlfriend and owned an old car. She had left school at 15, was training as a beautician and was making some extra income by selling beauty products. She was good at both. During her school years she had already shown initiative by finding work in the evenings and during school holidays. This was just as well because she did not like school much.

The situation of her brother Patrick was quite different. He was 22 years old but still at home. He was doing the final year of an arts degree and was planning to continue at university for further studies. Patrick was a good student but was unable to pay his own way with a scholarship and the income of odd jobs during holidays. He had a girlfriend, who also was at university, but they were not planning to marry until he finished his degree. Joan, who was younger, was functioning as an adult, while her brother Patrick, in spite of his 22 years, was like an adolescent in many ways.

As you can see from this example, the increased need for knowledge and skills to find work has a direct impact on growing up. This often results in a mismatch between the physical development of the person, completed during the teenage years, and their position in the family and society. Patrick is artificially maintained in a dependent role in the third decade of his life. This can produce tension and unhappiness.

Physical development

Early and late maturation

Everyone knows that not all children's bodies mature at the same time. Some are quite precocious while others are late maturers. Nevertheless, changes follow the same pattern and begin with the 'growth spurt'. On average, girls start maturing two years earlier than boys. Different parts of the body grow at different speeds. For example, the legs grow faster than the arms. The shape of the body also changes. Boys develop wider shoulders and muscle while girls' bodies become rounder because of an increase in body fat.

There has been a shift to maturing earlier during the last hundred years. While most girls had their first period at about the age of 15 in the 1880s, the average age was two years earlier in the 1970s and these days it is not rare for menstruation to start at 10 or 11 years. This is thought to be due to improvements in nutrition and health.

Because of the enormity and lack of harmony of the physical changes, adults should not be surprised when teenagers worry a lot about the way they look. Just remember how you felt when you were that age.

Is early maturing an advantage?

Consider the complex interactions that take place at this time. For example, Adam is 12 years old. His voice has already broken and he has been through the growth spurt. His standing among his peers, most of whom still look like children, has improved because he is taller and brawnier and his shape is more adult-like. Adam is now more able to play sports and is stronger. Because he looks older he is given more responsibility at home and at school. This helps him to grow in confidence and become more relaxed and good-natured. Obviously, for Adam, as for most boys, maturing earlier is advantageous.

> *Maturing early is advantageous for boys. For girls, it is advantageous to mature at the same time as their peers.*

Take now the case of Claire, a previously well-adjusted girl who had been an average student. She had her growth spurt and her periods at the age of 11 years. By 12 she looked like a fully developed adolescent, well ahead of her peers. Her body shape had changed and she had gained weight. She felt fat and unattractive and began dieting on and off. Self-consciousness about her body and shape led her to avoid sports and physical education. She felt out of place with girls of her own age and began joining in with girls two or three years older, who shared her interests and concerns. These older girls were more streetwise and enjoyed more freedom. She began receiving attention from older boys. Their interest flattered and confused her. She did not know how to respond, but her involvement with boys grew at the expense of her school work. Claire also began smoking, against her parents' wishes, to be like her friends. All these issues created conflict and tension when Claire's parents did not allow her to come home as late as her friends did or tried to enforce homework. Screaming matches, slamming of doors and tearful episodes became an everyday occurrence. Her interest in school work and her marks declined. It is clear that for Claire, as for many girls, maturing early is not advantageous.

Most teenagers cope well with puberty no matter when it happens. I give these two examples to illustrate that similar processes can have a vastly different impact on different children, and on boys and girls. However, boys who mature early tend to do better than late maturers while the opposite is true for girls. Girls do best if they mature at the same time as their peers.

Can anything be done to influence growth?

Although it is rare, some children who do not grow and remain small may need hormonal treatment. A paediatrician's opinion will put your mind at rest if this is worrying you.

Regular physical exercise and participation in sports help physical growth as well as socialisation and self-esteem. The time parents spend involving their young children in sports activities pays off during adolescence. In particular, girls who participate in sports find it easier to maintain a lower proportion of body fat, have fewer concerns about their body shape and are more confident.

Intellectual changes

As children become older they are able to resolve increasingly difficult problems and learn from experience. Children can understand and use abstract ideas from an early age. However, at about the age of 12 a new universe full of exciting, but also frightening, possibilities opens up. Their mind expands and is able to perform abstract thought, for example considering different options and thinking about thoughts and ideas. Most teenagers dive headfirst into this magic world stretching out in front of them. Such a newfound ability often leads to an infatuation with social, political, philosophical or religious causes. It results also in an increasing concern about the meaning of life, in brooding and withdrawal. Because of their penchant for questioning everything, idealism may turn into scepticism. The security experienced in earlier years can give way to intellectual anguish and doubt: who am I? This stage can be particularly stressful for adopted children, whose need to know about their natural parents reawakens.

Most parents find their teenage child's inclination to question their values and decisions particularly annoying and it often causes arguments. If you see this as your children exercising their intellectual muscles so that they become fitter to cope with the world outside the family, this stage will be more bearable.

Bad decisions

But how can they be so clever, yet make so many mistakes? Obviously, being able to think logically is no guarantee of better decisions. Having a good car does not mean the driver will not speed or go through a red traffic light. However, it does reduce the chances of the car breaking down and not arriving at the destination. Teenagers make 'bad' decisions because their priorities are often

> *Teenagers' priorities are often different from those of their parents.*

different from those of their parents, not because they lack the logic to do it right. For instance, it is common for many adolescents to start smoking in spite of parental prohibitions and knowing full well that smoking is harmful to their health. Fitting in with the group may be more important for them at the time than parents' opinions or the dangers to their health.

Perceptions about the value and meaning of academic achievement also vary among adolescents and between boys and girls. Some teenagers believe that good marks at school are more a manifestation of a great intelligence than of motivation and effort. For them, achieving is the same as being intelligent. Consequently, adolescents with this belief do not strive as much as they could to succeed. This can also be influenced by peers, teachers and parents, and it may explain why girls tend to drop-off in maths and science in the last years of high school. Parents usually have higher expectations of boys than girls. The more understanding attitude of parents towards girls may give them the impression that they are not bright enough to really succeed. Parents, teachers and peers can all influence the belief that achievement is to a very large extent the result of personal effort, rather than luck or being gifted.

The quest for identity and autonomy

Jumping the gap from reliance on the family for everything (identity, security, food and shelter) to becoming an independent adult is not easy. It requires time and many attempts. Nevertheless, becoming independent persons with their own identity is one of the most important goals teenagers need to achieve. The trials and errors involved are characteristic of adolescence. Sometimes they go too far (e.g. by rejecting most family values) or, occasionally, not far enough (e.g. by not taking up opportunities for progress because these involve being away from home). For example, it is common for older adolescents to have stints at living away from home with friends until they finally settle their independent living situation.

In spite of the annoyance and worry produced by so many changes, you ought to see these attempts as your children's need to convince themselves that they can cope away from the security and comfort of the family. Returning home reassures them that you still care, that you can cope without them, and that they have not been rejected or forgotten. A young child who begins exploring the world needs to come and go, touching base to check that mother is still there. The security of her presence allows the child to move further each time.

The speed of this process can be accelerated or slowed down by other experiences. Children who have been away from the family for short periods of time, attending camps or spending time with relatives or friends, and who enjoyed such separations are more likely to feel confident about their ability to manage by themselves than a child who never had similar experiences.

Power struggles

'Why don't you take to cooking?' [asked mother]

'Take to cooking,' I retorted with scorn. 'The fire that a fellow has to endure on that old oven would kill a horse, and the grit and dirt of clearing it up grinds on my very nerves. Besides, if I do ever want to do any extra fancy cooking, we either can't afford the butter or the currants, or else the eggs are too scarce! Cook be grannied!'

'Sybylla, Sybylla, you are getting very vulgar!'

'What on earth does it matter if I'm vulgar or not. I can feed calves and milk and grind out my days here just as well vulgar as unvulgar,' I answered savagely.

'That I should ever have nurtured a child to grow up like this.'

(...) I am a piece of machinery, which, not understanding, my mother winds up the wrong way, setting all the wheels of my composition going in creaking discord (...) I certainly was utterly different to any girl I had seen or known. What was the hot wild spirit which surged within me?

Miles Franklin, 1990, *My Brilliant Career, My Career Goes Bung*, Angus & Robertson, Sydney, pp. 31–3

Adolescents' search for identity can be rather infuriating for everyone else. They often affirm their fledgling self by rejecting family's, school's or society's values. If parents like their hair long, they cut it short. If school expects short hair, they either try to grow it too long or shave their head. If parents are religious people, they become non-believers. The list could go on. This is a bit of a repetition of the 'terrible twos', when children discover the power of the word 'no' and use it with gusto on every possible occasion. The fact is, adolescents need to emphasise they are themselves by rebelling and being different from, or the opposite of, what their parents are or want them to be. It is also an attempt to exercise power. More often than not this is a transitory phase that does not last long. When teenagers actually develop a sense of their own identity, the need to emphasise their differences from the family gradually vanishes.

This struggle can cause tension and arguments. Often, friction arises when parents try to set reasonable limits. In these circumstances, you need to hold your ground, be firm and matter-of-fact. However, it is essential that parents see this struggle as a normal stage of their child's development and avoid getting caught in battles for control. The latter happens when parents take their teenager's behaviour too seriously and see it as a challenge to their authority, or as their child's lack of 'respect' for them.

These power struggles can be particularly difficult and painful if there is one absent parent. This parent tends to be idealised and the parent living with the teenager devalued. This can be quite hurtful for the remaining parent and complicates discipline.

Personal space

Adolescents' need for personal space is another aspect of their search for autonomy. Many teenagers become more secretive after puberty, spend more time in their rooms and resent being questioned about what they do or feel. Frequently they keep diaries to which they confide their aspirations, hopes and disappointments. Parents should respect children's privacy (unless important issues of safety are involved) and give teenagers the emotional elbow room they require. Sometimes this is not easy. Parents often miss the closeness they used to have and perceive this withdrawal as rejection, or think that their child no longer loves or cares for them. This false perception can produce grief or anger that, in turn, has the potential to poison the relationship.

Mood changes

Most parents know that teenagers are moody. When they are happy, they are on top of the world. When they are unhappy, they are miserable. Their mood can change from moment to moment, often triggered by apparently trivial events.

Self-esteem and self-concept

The development of self-esteem and of an image of themselves that fits their attributes and shortcomings is another aspect of adolescence. Teenagers' self-concept becomes more sophisticated and subtle than children's. Their image of themselves is no longer global, as it was during childhood, but varies according to areas of their personality. For example, they are able to realise they are very good at maths but not good in English, or good relating to people and not so good in school work, or good at school work and poor at sports. At the same time, adolescents become more aware of whom they would like to be. An appreciation of the differences between the ideal and the real self can be a source of unhappiness. Coming to terms with this is an important task of growing up.

A global sense of self-esteem develops gradually during adolescence. This is not just the average of the self-concepts in a variety of areas (e.g. very good in maths, lousy at sports, can tell good jokes) but goes further. Being liked by peers and being physically attractive, particularly in the case of girls, are important components. That is why pimples, physical shape and weight become the source of so much concern and misery at this age and can have a negative effect on self-esteem. On the contrary, popularity with peers or being accepted as part of a group reinforces teenagers' sense of worth.

The development of self-esteem, however, is a complex process that does not depend only on experiences during adolescence, although these are important. Self-esteem is eroded by negative events. Bad experiences during infancy or early childhood, particularly poor bonding or attachment to a parent, can make self-esteem more fragile. Because positive attachments provide emotional protection in periods of stress and reduce anxiety, they help teenagers cope with negative experiences and protect their self-esteem.

Risk-taking, grandiosity

Insecurity, hesitancy and self-doubt exist side by side with grandiosity in teenagers. They often exaggerate the extent of their competence by thinking that they are right and everyone who does not agree with them is wrong, or that nothing can happen to them, even if they do quite dangerous things. Taking risks is very much a part of what being a teenager is all about. This sense of invulnerability is probably necessary for adolescents to have enough confidence to test the limits of what they can do. Testing limits – family's, society's and their own – is an important experience through which they learn the boundaries of their skill and consolidate their self-esteem. However, parents need to set and enforce appropriate limits. If this behaviour is left unchecked it can become self-destructive. Parents also need to provide their teenage children with outlets for this drive through sport or creative activities.

Occasionally, grandiosity takes the form of competition with parents. This happens more often with sons and fathers. When handled well, it results in children having a more realistic view of their parents' virtues and shortcomings. Such a view will gradually replace the earlier, unrealistic image of parents as all-powerful, perfect people.

Smoking, alcohol, drugs

Drinking alcohol or using marijuana occasionally is part of teenagers' penchant for testing rules and taking risks. Regrettably, recreational drug use has become a feature of the lifestyle of many adolescents these days. Around one in five 18-year-olds are daily smokers, most consume alcohol at least weekly and up to one in three use marijuana once a week.

Most adolescent drug and alcohol use takes place in social situations. The attitudes and values of friends have a strong influence on this but the behaviour of parents is important also. Conflict within the family and at school increases the risk of problematic use of alcohol and drugs. In this context a young person is attracted to other troubled teenagers and assumes their lifestyle, values and drug use patterns. Shyness and excessive worry about social situations can also lead to alcohol abuse (drinking to 'relax' or to 'get courage').

Friends, social relationships

Social relationships are an indispensable part of our lives, particularly during adolescence. Friends and the peer group become much more important during this period, so much so that young adolescents are reluctant to go out or be seen with parents. As a result they spend more leisure time with friends than with family. Being part of, and accepted by, a group becomes extremely important.

Parents and teachers believe that peers' opinions are listened to more often than theirs. Teenagers appear to think that speaking, dressing and doing what friends do is vital. Although the pressure to conform to what other children of the same age think or do is strong, this is hardly a one-way process. More often than not adolescents are influenced by friends, but friends they have chosen in the first place or with whom they identify. Nevertheless, friends can greatly affect teenagers, both for good and bad.

> *Not having access to good friends increases the chances of becoming involved with bad ones.*

Facilitating or encouraging children to become involved in sports and group activities will allow them to meet and relate to well-adjusted people of their own age and with similar values. Not having opportunities to meet good friends increases the chances of becoming involved with bad ones.

The increasing importance of friendships and spending more time with peers does not necessarily mean that teenagers become distant from their family, or that they are no longer influenced by parents. Undoubtedly, there are more clashes about curfew times, amount of telephone use, style of dress or hair, or other relatively trivial matters that can create an impression of alienation or inter-generational conflict. However, most teenagers have a strong attachment to their parents. They trust and care for them and turn to them for advice on important matters. Also, they seek support from parents in difficult situations. The relationship with parents is certainly different from what it used to be when children were younger: it has grown in depth and maturity.

Sexuality

Sexual behaviour is often the aspect of teenagers' conduct that worries parents most. Early parenthood and sexually transmitted diseases such as AIDS are certainly a risk during this time. Sexual maturity also changes the parent–child relationship. The young man or woman you see now cannot be treated like the baby you nursed not that long ago.

Children acquire a sense of being male or female during the first two or three years of life. This results in different social interactions for boys and girls. Girls are usually more interested in playing with dolls and clothes or caring for younger siblings, while boys show rough-and-tumble play and are more interested in tools and construction. There is a small link between sexual-role activities during early childhood and adult sexual behaviour. For instance, boys who have no interest in rough-and-tumble play are slightly more prone to become gay. Transsexuals, individuals who see themselves as having a different gender from the one they have in their bodies, describe a sexual identity dating back to early childhood ('I always felt that I was a girl trapped in a boy's body').

Hormones drive the escalation in sexual motivation and interests during puberty. The mode of expression, however, varies according to the child and according to the cultural values of the family and society where they live. Sexual urges can be controlled or sublimated into other constructive activities while the young person achieves educational or life goals. Masturbation seems to have been one main outlet for the sexual drive in the past. More recently, however, sexual intercourse appears to have become increasingly frequent among teenagers.

Dating also begins at this time. Dating is a ritual through which males and females learn to relate to and know each other. It usually involves sexual attraction and may include a variety of sexual activities, such as kissing and petting. Once children are pubertal, or reach a certain age, they are pressured by peers to date. Generally, boys tend to look for sexual adventure and have more partners than girls. Young women tend to look for romantic relationships and are more likely than boys to remain faithful to one partner at a time.

Talking about sex

It is essential that parents talk to their children about sex in a frank and open manner, and it is better to do this earlier than later. Do not deceive yourself or hide your head in the sand thinking that 'they are still too young' or 'my children would never do such a thing'. Knowing that they learn at school – or from magazines or friends – some of the technical aspects of reproduction, sex and sexually transmitted diseases is no justification for avoiding the subject. Start this process early, when young children ask for the first time where babies come from, and gradually build on that according to their age. All along, you need to convey the message that love and sex are wonderful gifts. Avoid threats and scare tactics as these often backfire. When the children are close to puberty, talk to them about intimacy and how this is achieved, from physical contact to kissing and intercourse. Help them understand that sex is more than just intercourse and that there are ways of expressing their sexuality without having intercourse. Always stress the positive but make sure they also know the risks. For example, they should know that drinking too much alcohol at parties can make people lose the ability to reason and take risks (such as having sex or unprotected sex) they would not have taken if they were sober.

Many parents find it very hard to talk about sex with their children. Generally, girls feel more comfortable discussing this topic with their mothers and boys with their fathers. Take advantage of a particular event (e.g. someone getting pregnant, a relevant piece of news or movie) to bring up the subject. Avoid giving a lecture. Talk about your own experiences – what you felt when you fell in love for the first time or had a crush on someone – and take it from there. Talk about contraception, the pill and condoms. If you just can't talk about these issues, have someone else you and your children trust, such as a relative or the family doctor, discuss it with them.

What influences the initiation of sexual activity?

Apart from hormones, the initiation of sexual activity is strongly influenced by friends, as well as social expectations given rise to by television shows, movies and magazines.

Characteristics that increase the probability of a child beginning sexual activity early include low self-esteem, poor achievement at school, lack of trust and communication with parents, involvement in other activities that are socially disapproved of, such as smoking, drinking or delinquency, and a lack of religious commitment.

Teenagers who start sexual intercourse early are less likely to use contraceptives and more likely to become parents. Most of these pregnancies are unwanted, although some young women actually seek to become pregnant to get out of an intolerable family situation. Some hope that having a child may save a relationship, although it never does.

WHAT CAN PARENTS DO TO HELP ADOLESCENTS AVOID PREMATURE SEXUAL ACTIVITY?

- Provide a stable and caring family atmosphere.
- Encourage trust and acceptance.
- Set consistent and reasonable limits.
- Don't use television indiscriminately as a sitter.
- Know where and with whom younger teenagers are at all times.
- Help their children find good friends.
- Talk frankly about sexual matters, including contraception and sexually transmitted diseases.
- Be a good role model.
- Keep children occupied in sports and other activities they enjoy.
- Ensure they attend a school that matches their abilities and personality (this is particularly important for children who are good at doing things with their hands but are not good at language or arithmetic).
- Seek professional help if their children are depressed or start abusing alcohol.

Sexual identity

Development of a sexual identity is a major part of the broader adolescent task of finding out who one is or wants to be, although this process starts much earlier. Some teenagers may feel puzzled by their feelings towards friends of the same sex and about their sexual orientation. This does not necessarily mean they are gay. Others, who clearly feel sexually aroused by persons of the same sex, go through a good deal of turmoil coming to terms with this. Their parents' understanding or lack of it can make the process easier or more painful for them.

Yes, today's teenagers are different

Many parents say that today's teenagers are 'different'. Although we all tend to idealise the past, this statement rings true. Adolescents in the third millennium not only are targeted by the media like never before, have unparalleled and immediate access to all kinds of information and live in families and societies that are changing dramatically, but they also experience changes in their bodies earlier than before.

These days children, particularly girls, reach puberty much earlier than a hundred or even fifty years ago. This means that they are confronted by the urges and needs of an adult at a younger age. Many parents experience the rollercoaster of their teenagers living through the excitement of first love, the anxiety of first sexual intercourse, the pain of the first break-up, and all this by the age of 14 or 15 years. Regrettably, maturation of the body does not mean that mind, knowledge and experience have grown at the same speed. In this context, it is easy to understand the increase in youth depression.

This certainly places extra demands on parents and children. 'Being a prime minister can be a tough job, but I always think being a parent is probably tougher,' said Tony Blair, the British Prime Minister, after his son Euan, 16, was arrested in July 2000 for being drunk and disorderly.

Some rules for dealing with teenagers

Some principles that parents often find helpful are described in this chapter. Although they do not deal with all possible situations, they provide a framework you can adapt to your specific circumstances. These principles should be applied with flexibility and commonsense.

Evolution not revolution

Be predictable.

Adolescence is an evolutionary process. It requires adjustments by the child and by the parents. The worst you can do is wake up one day realising that Helen is adolescent and decide to treat her differently from that day on. You can't change the way you deal with your teenage child suddenly and completely. This would feel false and unnatural to the child and you probably couldn't carry it through. If you have given your children much freedom it would be counterproductive to change your style by becoming too strict or controlling. If you had been very strict you can't all of a sudden become permissive. You will need to adjust your discipline and expectations to the specific needs of your teenage child gradually, in a way you feel comfortable with.

Do not panic

Teenagers often experience conflicting emotions and drives and this can confuse them. As a consequence their mind and feelings often

> **Children are reassured if parents appear to be in control.**

change. It is important for them to see that parents are, at least outwardly, clear and secure about their rules and expectations, that parents do not panic or change their mind with every minor crisis. Although children may appear to resent it, deep down they feel reassured, just as a lost traveller feels comforted by the sight of a signpost, even if it indicates that the destination is still far away.

Panic and over-reacting get in the way of your relationship with your children. For example, if your 13-year-old daughter Helen asks you in passing a question about sex, you may immediately worry that she is having sex or even that she is pregnant. You then start asking questions and think she is keeping something secret from you. An innocent remark can end up in a dreadful argument. It would be much better to answer the question without fuss as well as you can. Probably Helen will feel reassured by your trust and matter-of-fact attitude and will explain why she was asking.

There is no 'right' way

Many parents think that they don't know how to bring up children and search for the 'right' way of doing so. There is no such thing. 'Knowing' is not a guarantee of being able to put knowledge into practice either: probably you have read that so-called 'experts' are often not very good parents for their own children. Ways of bringing up children vary quite a lot from culture to culture, and yet they achieve similar results whatever the style. The problems faced by parents in a small country town or on a rural property are quite different from those encountered by parents in a crowded suburb of a large city. This does not mean that you can't improve parenting skills or that such endeavour is pointless. It means that worrying too much about parenting or doing it inflexibly can do more harm than good.

Every child is different

I am not a good gardener. Most plants I touch seem to wither and die. However, I did learn that each plant has specific needs. Some do

> **Different children need to be treated differently.**

well in good, fertile soil, some don't. Some need plenty of direct sunlight, others are burnt by it. One plant requires lots of care while the other thrives on neglect. Similarly, most parents know that no two children are the same, that different children need to be treated differently.

Although you can apply some basic principles, children vary so much that something which works very well with John may not work at all with Nathan, and vice versa. It is essential that you adapt your discipline and expectations of your children to match their personality and attributes. Don't do things just because that's the way you were brought up or because you read it in a book. Your knowledge of what makes your children tick, flexibility and commonsense are the best guides. This also means that brothers and sisters are not necessarily treated the same. Parents need to be, and appear to be, fair to all their children. However, privileges, duties, discipline and expectations need to be tailored according to each one's age, personality and maturity.

Learn from your mistakes

No one is perfect. We all make plenty of mistakes and this is nowhere clearer than in bringing up children. Children know and understand this and make allowances for parents. You don't need to worry too much about making mistakes.

What you can't do is repeat the same errors again and again. When that happens you become destructive and this often creates a vicious cycle from which it is difficult to break out. This can happen if you have not dealt with something inside that is hurting, such as old emotional wounds.

Karen is a successful career woman who lives with her son Jason. Karen and her husband separated when Jason was 2 years old. There had been very little contact with the father, who had remarried. Jason was a happy, affectionate child who did well at school and had many friends. Karen's relationship with her son had been great and rewarding. She had given him freedom and responsibility to which he had responded in a mature way. However, things began to change when Jason reached puberty at the age of 12 years. Karen became increasingly critical of Jason, putting him down often. She became more controlling and denied him freedoms he had enjoyed before. Jason reacted to this by becoming angry, argumentative and defiant. Quarrels became frequent and Jason began coming home well after curfew times set by Karen. His school grades slipped and he joined in with other troubled and troublesome teenagers. One night he went out and did not come home until the next day. Karen was ill with worry and called the police in desperation. She and Jason had a terrible row after he returned. Karen almost went into a state of shock when Jason talked about going to live with his father for a while.

When talking about this incident with a good friend, Karen blurted out that she felt threatened by her son's growing up. She felt that Jason, who physically had begun looking remarkably similar to his father, was going to betray and leave her, like his father had done. It transpired that the ex-husband had had several affairs while she was nursing Jason and had finally left her after bitter arguments and recriminations. When Jason reached puberty he became the object of all the pent-up anger and resentment she had been hiding for years. Karen was aware to some extent of what was happening, but she could not help becoming overwhelmed by these feelings.

Build on the positive

It is said that familiarity breeds contempt. It certainly happens in families that people often take for granted many things about each other. For example, if one evening meal is too salty or overcooked or has something else wrong with it, everyone complains. No one appears to have noticed that for the rest of the week, or month, meals were well prepared, succulent and nutritious. Such behaviour is very disheartening for the cook.

> *Look for, and acknowledge with praise or rewards, what your child does well.*

The same applies to teenagers. Although they are often helpful and work hard at school, some parents find it difficult to notice and acknowledge these positive things and fail to reward their children with well-deserved praise. On the other hand, when the children do something wrong they are reprimanded, criticised or put down. 'You did not get a better mark because you are lazy.' 'You never help.' 'You are only good to spend money.' These remarks are unhelpful and discouraging. Parents can achieve much more by focusing on the positive things, on their children's assets rather than their liabilities. Some parents think this is 'bribing' them to do the right thing. That is not the case.

The same applies to expectations. It would be almost comic to see a father encouraging and expecting his son, who is of very small stature and likes horses, to become a basketball player. It would be more realistic to push him in the direction of becoming a jockey!

You are the boss

There are many management styles in business. Some managers are authoritarian while others manage by consensus or by involving workers in decision making. No matter what the management style an enterprise has, at the end of the day someone has to make decisions and set priorities. The same happens in a family. Parents have the ultimate responsibility of deciding what should be done and need to feel confident about making these decisions. The way you reach a decision will vary according to your style and personality, but you need to be able to make decisions and put them into practice.

It is quite damaging for a family when parents are unable to make decisions. Things drift along aimlessly and circumstances end up making decisions for the family. When parents feel insecure and give up on decisions after the first challenge from their teenage child an atmosphere of confusion and uncertainty is created. This encourages adolescents' rebelliousness and gives the impression that parents' just don't care. Being firm is particularly important if your child's safety is at risk.

However, being the boss does not mean that you have to be rigid or inflexible. You will need to negotiate, to listen to your children's reasons. In many cases you will need to compromise, to give a bit.

Have few rules

Every family needs to have some rules to function. However, teenagers ought to take increasing responsibility for their own behaviour and so the fewer the rules, the better. Usually, if they do the right thing it is because their conscience tells them to or because they respect you, not because they are afraid of breaking a rule. You should certainly avoid having rules for every possible eventuality. Most families, however, need rules covering things such as when to arrive home, about going out, dating, telephone use, homework, use of cars or driving, pocket money and household duties. These rules should be discussed with the teenagers and they should be allowed to give their opinion, which needs to be taken into account.

Be consistent

Can you imagine what it would be like for a football player if a referee changed the rules all the time or if there were two referees on the playing field with two different sets of rules? Chaotic. The match could not take place. This can happen in families. It results in children feeling confused to start with, and doing what they want in the end. Even if rules are not right, if they are applied consistently they allow the game to take place. Parents need to be consistent individually and together. It is disastrous when one parent says something and the other contradicts or undermines that decision. Consistency also means that you need to follow through your decisions and do your best to ensure your children abide by them.

Don't go into battle if you can't win

Someone said that a withdrawal on time is as good as a victory. No sane general will go into battle knowing he is going to lose. You know your strengths and weaknesses better than anyone else, as well as those of your child. It is important to avoid getting into arguments that you can't win. If you become involved in a battle with your teenage child, you need to have confidence that you are going to win it.

Seek your children's opinions

In most cases teenagers are intelligent, rational and have the best interests of the family at heart. It makes sense to get them involved in decision making by asking their opinion in matters that affect them. This may include discussion about such things as an appropriate punishment for something, or the conditions under which they would be allowed to attend a party, or whether they should attend this or that school. Children's opinions need to be taken into consideration when making substantial decisions that are going to affect the family, such as job changes that require relocation. The final decision is up to the parents, but knowing their children's thoughts on the matter will help them make a more informed decision. This process will also reduce the chances of children undermining or rebelling against the decision.

Explain the reasons for your decisions

Try as much as possible to explain the reasons for your decisions to your children. There are few things that infuriate adolescents more than parents saying 'because I say so'. Parents do not usually make decisions on a whim, but for very good reasons. Safety may be the concern behind asking children to return home during daylight. Not having done their homework, as previously agreed, may be the reason for not allowing them to go out. Even if they don't seem too impressed at the time, explain.

THE DON'TS OF DEALING WITH ADOLESCENTS

- Don't scream or lose control.
- Don't be unfair.
- Don't be unpredictable.
- Don't be violent.
- Don't change your mind all the time.
- Don't put them down.
- Don't be afraid to admit that you are wrong.
- Don't nag or go on and on.
- If you find yourself doing all these things, don't forget you are only human.

Normality and disorder

3

W hat is normal and what is abnormal is the focus of this chapter. This will help you know when to seek advice or help for your teenage child and when you are worrying unnecessarily.

Many parents feel confused about what is normal and what is abnormal because adolescents can present a bewildering array of behaviours. Is Joanne's moodiness an indication that she has a depression or is it within the realms of normality? Is Nicholas's infatuation with UFOs just that, an infatuation, or is it a sign of something more sinister? Is Eliza's concern about her weight and figure very much like that of any other teenager or is she developing anorexia nervosa? Are these problems just a stage they are going through or something that will require help or treatment? How to know? These are not rhetorical questions. Knowing when to seek advice or treatment may shorten the duration of problems and reduce your child's suffering – and yours.

To make things worse, parents often hear that 'all teenagers are crazy' and that 'no one can understand them'. Teachers or friends may tell you that your adolescent child has 'emotional problems' or is 'acting out'. Acting out is a psychological defence mechanism in which adolescents deal with emotional conflict or stress by doing something (such as getting drunk) rather than talking about it or becoming upset.

Bruce's parents had been concerned about him for some time. They loved him dearly and had tried to go out of their way to accommodate his preoccupation with tidiness and cleanliness. They had allowed him to have his own towels and soap, which Bruce protected jealously, and to spend a lot of time in the bathroom, even though this inconvenienced everyone else in the house. Because of his careful and complicated washing rituals, he was regularly late for school, although he woke up at first light. He often caused his parents to be late for work as well. What at first, when he was 9 years old, seemed to be a virtue (everyone was amazed at how clean and tidy his room was) became a nuisance later on. When his parents tried to push him to be quicker, Bruce became angry, upset or threw a tantrum. He became even slower and his rituals more convoluted. By the age of 13 it was such a problem that it was wearing down the whole family. His parents' love was turning increasingly into frustration. They finally realised there was something really wrong when Bruce's grades began to fall behind, when his teachers began complaining he had not done his assignments, when he began refusing to go out with his friends ('who knows what they have been touching') and when he began to refuse meals if he had not cooked them himself because he did not trust anyone else to be clean enough.

Does Bruce have a psychological disorder or can his behaviour, though extreme, be considered within the normal range? Is he emotionally disturbed or psychotic? Does he lack social skills? Was he brought up properly? What can be done to help him? What is going to happen to him when he becomes older? These are some of the questions that need an answer.

Psychological disorder

There is a lot of argument about which psychological problems are 'serious', and there are many ways of defining psychological (or psychiatric or mental) disorder. For example, what may be a mental illness from a medical point of view may not be so from a legal perspective. Nor are 'psychological' disorders necessarily distinct from 'physical' illnesses, for there is much overlap between them. Physical illnesses can cause psychiatric symptoms (e.g. people who are intoxicated or febrile can have hallucinations) and many psychological conditions, such as schizophrenia and obsessive compulsive disorder, are caused by subtle abnormalities in the brain.

From a practical perspective there are two characteristics that indicate that someone may have a psychological illness: when behaviours, experiences or feelings become so intense or persistent that they are abnormal (a psychological syndrome), and when as a result of these emotions or experiences the person is distressed or becomes disabled.

A *psychological syndrome* is when a group of symptoms occurs, persists and changes together over time. In the case of Bruce (see the box on page 35), this syndrome was characterised by his thoughts that he might be contaminated, that things had to be organised in precise ways and by his irresistible need to wash himself or tidy up.

When emotions or behaviours are too intense and persistent they also become a psychological syndrome. For example, it is normal to feel unhappy at times, particularly if you have suffered a loss or disappointment. However, if unhappiness becomes enduring, if you feel unhappy most of the day, every day for a period of time, it is abnormal and you may have a depressive syndrome.

> *Subjective distress and disability are the hallmarks of mental disorder.*

Distress means emotional pain, worry, fear or unhappiness, while *disability* means that the adolescent's capacity to perform at school according to his potential, to relate to peers and to live within the family are impaired. In Bruce's case, his continuous worry caused him to become easily upset (distress), and his symptoms interfered with his performance at school, got in the way of his family's routine and prevented him from joining his friends in social activities (disability). In the same way, someone who is persistently unhappy may also lose interest and motivation at work, find it hard to concentrate and become impatient and irritable. These symptoms produce considerable suffering (distress) and result in problems at work and with loved ones (disability).

When teenagers show intense emotional pain, unreasonable, inappropriate fear or unhappiness that persists for some time, these are indications that they may be suffering from a psychological problem. If you are uncertain, talk about it with your child's teachers and with your child. A negative change in the way adolescents behave or in their personality or routine are important signs that something may not be right. Clues to look for include:

- marked decline in school performance
- school non-attendance, even if it is because of minor physical complaints
- marked change in the usual behaviour at home (isolation, not talking to others in the house)
- withdrawal from friends or social activities
- marked changes in sleep pattern, eating or weight
- evidence of alcohol or marijuana use
- frequent tantrums, outbursts of anger, aggression or disobedience
- persistent sadness, excessive crying
- frequent talk about death or about life not being worth living
- excessive or irrational fears or worries
- self-destructive acts such as self-cutting or drug overdoses.

Descriptions of specific symptoms that characterise the more common types of adolescents' disorders appear in later chapters.

A CRISIS IN ADOLESCENT MENTAL HEALTH?

The nation is facing a public crisis in mental health for infants, children and adolescents. Many children have mental health problems that interfere with normal development and functioning. In the United States, one in ten children and adolescents suffer from mental illness severe enough to cause some level of impairment. Yet, in any given year, it is estimated that about one in five children receive mental health services. Unmet need for services remains as high now as it was 20 years ago. Recent evidence compiled by the World Health Organisation indicates that by the year 2020, childhood neuropsychiatric disorders will rise proportionately by over 50 per cent, internationally, to become one of the five most common causes of morbidity, mortality, and disability among children.

Source: *Report of the Surgeon General's Conference on Children's Mental Health: A National Action Agenda.* Washington, DC, 2000.
www.surgeongeneral.gov/cmh/cmhreport.pdf

Psychological disorders during adolescence

Mental disorders are common during adolescence. As many as 15 per cent of all teenagers suffer from a psychiatric illness at one time or another. Occasionally these conditions might be minor, such as fear of heights, but in about 10 per cent the disorder is serious enough to need treatment. The other side of the coin is that the majority of teenagers, up to 85 per cent of them, are well adjusted and without serious psychological problems.

> *The majority of adolescents are well adjusted and without serious problems.*

Psychological disorders should not be dismissed lightly. They can have consequences that go far beyond the effects of the condition itself. Mental disorders get in the way of normal development, producing gaps and long-term deficits. They interfere with schooling, with friendships and with family life. This can result in low self-esteem, ongoing resentment and bad habits. Psychological disorders not only decrease the quality of life but also make a premature death more likely. The most tragic example of this is suicide.

Adolescents with mental health problems are often disliked or rejected by their peers, are more prone to fail at school and drop out. They underachieve professionally and are more inclined to smoke cigarettes, to abuse alcohol or drugs and to become involved in antisocial or delinquent activities.

Bad news seldom comes alone. Many of these troubled teenagers do not have just one problem. Often they have several simultaneously. Having one disorder increases the risk of having other problems. For example, adolescents who are hyperactive (have attention deficit hyperactivity disorder) are more likely than their peers to have conduct problems, learning difficulties, depression and to abuse alcohol.

Mental health problems afflict not only adolescents but also adults. It might surprise you, but it is widely accepted that about one in three persons will suffer from a severe mental health problem in their lifetime. Half of them will have already shown symptoms of the condition by the age of 16 years. Therefore, early identification and treatment are essential to prevent much suffering and disability.

The public at large, health authorities and government have begun to realise the seriousness of these problems only recently and so few resources are allocated to the problem. Parents who have experienced the distress and disability first-hand can do much to lobby government.

What causes mental disorders?

Most people tend to blame very specific incidents (a disappointment, a loss, a traumatic experience) for emotional or behavioural problems. It is seldom that simple. There is always an interaction between life experiences, the adolescent's personality and temperament, inherited vulnerabilities and environmental factors, such as the presence or absence of good family support. The relative contribution of the various factors to the development of a specific disorder will vary in each individual. Further, there are also protective factors. Discovering them is particularly important because they increase young people's resilience.

For example, a person might have an inherited predisposition to diabetes. If the person has a good diet, does regular exercise and keeps weight down (protective factors), the chances of developing diabetes will be lower than for someone else with the same predisposition who does not exercise, has a poor diet and is overweight. However, the harmful habits of the second person might be largely the consequence of having grown up in a family in which these unhealthy tendencies were promoted, or result from ignorance about their potential harm or personality traits (such as poor impulse control), or to all these circumstances together.

The same happens with mental health problems. A young boy may be shy and sensitive. This boy will probably grow up into a competent, happy adult. The chances of this positive outcome will be higher if his parents are supportive but encourage him to become involved with peers and to participate in games and activities, even though he is initially reluctant (protective factors). However, if his fearful temperament is reinforced by parents who worry too much about everyday things, who are overprotective and give in at the first sign of resistance on his part, then this boy is more likely to develop an anxiety disorder. Suffering from a physical illness that requires hospitalisation, having to change school several times, being the victim of bullying, and other traumatic experiences will also make him more prone to anxiety.

CIRCUMSTANCES THAT DECREASE THE RISK OF MENTAL HEALTH PROBLEMS (PROTECTIVE FACTORS)

- Good early attachment to a parental figure
- Good, regular temperament during infancy
- Stable, caring family
- Higher intelligence
- Repeated experiences of success at school and in other activities
- Being liked by peers
- Having friends who don't get into trouble
- Good physical health
- Lack of mental health problems or delinquency in the family

The effect of negative experiences varies greatly depending on the adolescent, on when they happen and on the context in which they occur. The loss of a parent, for example, can have vastly different effects on different children. Whether it happened through death or separation, whether it occurred following a period of marital conflict, and whether children were able to grieve the loss appropriately can influence the consequences. The timing of the loss is also important. If it occurs when teenagers are going through other important life changes, such as starting high school or having lost a job, it is likely to be more damaging. How close the children were to the parent and the meaning the children attach to the loss (do they blame themselves?) will also be relevant. Finally, the loss of the parent may put into motion a series of changes which could be more harmful for the child than the loss itself. For example, a divorce often results in a drop in the family income, in having to change residence or school (with the consequent loss of friends and emotional support), or in a step-parent appearing in the household. Clear-cut events such as a divorce can have very wide implications or trigger something like a chain reaction.

> *A teenager who was never exposed to stressful situations will be poorly equipped to cope with the normal wear and tear of life.*

It is important to know, however, that not all stressful experiences are harmful. In fact, teenagers who were never exposed to stressful situations will be ill-prepared to cope with the normal wear and tear of life. Shielding them from the realities of existence won't necessarily protect them. What makes the difference is not the lack of stressful experiences but whether these happen in an atmosphere in which the young person feels supported. Also, it is important that the incidents are not overwhelming, and the adolescents are able to adjust to them, giving them a sense of achievement and mastery.

Seeking help 4

This chapter guides you through the steps involved in seeking and getting help, from referral through the assessment interview and the processes of treatment. It also covers what you should do and what you and your child can expect at each stage.

There are a variety of professionals who can deal with adolescent mental health problems. These include child and adolescent psychiatrists, psychologists, paediatricians, social workers, general practitioners and school counsellors. Who the best person is will depend on the type of problem and its severity. If your child's problems occur mainly at school, then the school counsellor may be a good starting point. If, on the contrary, problems manifest themselves mainly at home, you might do better discussing the situation with your family doctor or other counsellor.

Services are provided by private practitioners, community health centres, adolescent services and specialised clinics. The last often have in-patient treatment programs. Specialised facilities usually have multi-disciplinary teams that include child and adolescent psychiatrists, psychologists and other medical and non-medical personnel. Some non-government organisations also run counselling and residential services for adolescents. Appendix B lists organisations where you can obtain more information about services.

> *The immense majority of persons who see a psychiatrist are not 'mad'.*

If possible, you should ensure that the professional, or clinician, you choose has knowledge, skills and experience in the assessment and treatment of adolescent disorders. Ask the person who recommends a professional to you, your family doctor or someone who has knowledge in the area. Professional colleges or associations may be of help. Satisfy yourself that your choice has appropriate qualifications, is registered and is a member of a learned body (professional association) that upholds ethical and professional standards.

Practitioners often have different skills as a result of their particular training and experience. Not all are equally qualified to treat all problems. Social workers, for example, often have skills in family therapy, while psychologists are expert in the administration of psychometric tests. Many parents are unclear about the roles of psychologists and psychiatrists. Some think that psychiatrists only deal with 'crazy' people. That is not the case. Most individuals treated by psychiatrists are not insane. However, psychiatrists are medically qualified and, as such, are able to assess the potential effects of physical illnesses, to perform a comprehensive evaluation and to prescribe medication if required.

The referral process

A referral is usually required before you can seek specialist advice or treatment, except in emergencies. If the situation is urgent and serious, you should take your child to the closest emergency service.

In the case of community health centres you can make the referral yourself by telephoning the centre. You will be asked a few questions to establish your concerns about your child, to ensure the type of help you need is available in that centre. If they are unable to help, they will give you information about who to contact. Most community health centres service a specific geographical area. You will need to find out which is the centre that services your suburb.

Most consultants and specialist facilities require referral by another professional, such as a general practitioner or a school counsellor, who has assessed the adolescent and felt that a more specialised service was required. The referring professional will be able to estimate the degree of urgency and can communicate this to the consultant. This is because there are few services and these concentrate their efforts on the more severe or complex cases. The professional making the referral will be expected to give a brief description of the problems and the service required, whether that is assessment, treatment with medication or a court report.

If the referral is done properly, it saves time and improves the chances of obtaining the most appropriate help for your child. However, getting an appointment is often difficult. It may take quite a few phone calls and some time. Occasionally, it becomes a very frustrating process because there are still few services for young people with mental health problems and they may be not well known or may have lengthy waiting lists. Nevertheless, if you are patient and persistent you will succeed.

Referral, however, is only the first step. You also need to find the right professional or clinician for your child. That professional will be one who is not only knowledgeable but also listens and appears supportive. Your child will need to feel reasonably comfortable with that person. For example, some adolescents feel more at ease with a female than a male clinician. Some of the aspects that you need to clarify include:

• What arrangements does this professional have to help you if a crisis arises? For example, how can he or she be contacted after business hours or between appointments?
• What will be the frequency and duration of appointments?
• What will be your or your family's involvement in the treatment?
• What problems are the main focus of the treatment? How will therapy lessen these problems? How long will the therapy last? How will progress be evaluated?
• What is the cost of treatment? Is this fully or partially covered by your health insurance? Is there a charge for missed appointments?

Finding out whether a professional is the right one or not may take more than one appointment. You also need to be realistic in your expectations. On the one hand, running from one clinician to another can do more harm than good. On the other, persisting with a therapist who is not helping or with whom your child does not get along is a waste of time.

Preparation for the initial interview

Preparing things well for the initial interview will save time and inconvenience. This may entail preparing your child, collecting relevant information and ensuring that all family members requested to attend can actually attend. You will also need to find out how much time you need to put aside for the initial assessment. Some clinicians may do it in one hour but the majority will require more time, either in one day or over several days.

Preparation of the adolescent

Most young people feel anxious or threatened about seeing a mental health professional. Regrettably, there is stigma attached to psychiatric illness and for many teenagers consulting a professional means that there is something wrong with them, that they are weak or crazy. However, all psychological treatments require some cooperation from the patient. Adolescents who are unwilling to do what is required of them, who do not give accurate information or who are overtly angry and hostile will make treatment impossible or even counterproductive. Therefore, teenagers should agree to attend, at the very least. No one would expect them to be thrilled by the prospect though. Deceiving them or taking adolescents to see a clinician under false pretences should be avoided. This creates anger and resentment, which can become insurmountable barriers for treatment now and in the future.

> *Deceiving adolescents /or taking them to the consultation under false pretences should be avoided.*

Most teenagers are intelligent and sensible enough to understand what is involved. Given some time, and frank and positive explanations, they will usually come around. Parents and professionals underestimate young people's ability to make sensible choices.

If, in spite of everything, your teenager is unwilling to go, it is better to delay the appointment until her attitude changes.

45

To do this you may need to involve persons who play an important role in her life, such as grandparents, teachers or friends. This, of course, does not apply if there is risk to her life or when she is so disturbed that she can't understand what is happening. However, such situations are rare. In some instances, teenagers, particularly if they are older, may realise that they have a problem and ask for help themselves, either directly or through their parents. It is important that parents help and support adolescents through this process, and respect their privacy if they want to be seen by the professional on their own. Clinicians will bring the parents into the assessment or treatment if they think it advisable.

HELPING ADOLESCENTS AGREE TO A PROFESSIONAL CONSULTATION

- Be encouraging and positive. Avoid critical statements such as 'I'm fed up with you. I'm going to take you to someone who will fix you or put you away.'
- Explain clearly the reasons for the consultation:
  - 'Your father, your teachers and I are concerned because you have been missing school, you have been very unhappy and unable to concentrate. This is not like you.'
  - 'I think you need help because you have not been your-self for some time. You don't seem to enjoy things any more. I was hoping this was something transitory but it is lasting too long and you seem to be getting worse.'
  - 'Talking to a professional who understands teenagers can help.'
  - 'I need advice too on how to help you and be a better parent.'
- Sometimes it helps when the problem is labelled as 'a family problem' and the whole family attends the first interview. This takes the focus off the adolescent.
- Ask whether your child would prefer to consult a male or female therapist. If possible, discuss the pros and cons of the various options (e.g. who the clinicians being considered are, their qualifications, who recommended them to you) and get your child's opinion.
- Describe the interview: when and where it will take place, how long it will last and what will happen.

- Encourage your teenager to be open and honest.
- Reassure the teenager about confidentiality, that you won't pressure the therapist to tell you what your child talks about and that clinicians are bound by professional confidentiality (except if the teenager's or someone else's life is in danger).

Preparing the family

Some services require that as many as possible of the family members living at home attend the interview. This is because having a perspective on the whole family helps the consultant understand the adolescent's problems better. The teenager's problems have an impact on other family members, and conflict among family members may have an effect on the adolescent's problems. In any case, it is essential that at least you and your partner attend the initial interview with your child.

In my experience fathers have more difficulties attending. They often claim to be too busy but the importance of the father's involvement, at least initially, cannot be emphasised enough. Fathers can add valuable information, ask questions to clarify issues, express their views and have the opportunity to hear first-hand the advice of the consultant. Clear statements can become blurred and confusing when heard second-hand. This will also help the father understand the rationale for treatment. Both parents' attendance at the consultation sends a message of support and concern to their child in this difficult situation.

Collecting information

The consultant will make decisions on the basis of the information you and your child provide. As is said about computers: 'garbage in, garbage out'. If you feed in the wrong information, you will get the wrong answer. Think about the problems beforehand. When did you first notice them? What else happened at the time? Gather school reports and take them with you, as teachers' comments in school reports are often helpful. Also, take along reports by other professionals, if you have them, as well as the results of any psychological or achievement tests.

The interview

The initial interview aims to get the necessary information to find out what problems, if any, your child has and what can be done about them. The problems need to be defined carefully before a treatment plan is established.

Clinicians will ask detailed questions about the concerns you have about your child and her symptoms. For example, if she is unhappy, they will ask when this unhappiness was first noticed. 'Is she unhappy all the time, most of the time or only some of the time?' 'Mornings or evenings?' 'Is she able to enjoy some activities?' 'What is the depth of her unhappiness?' 'Is she so unhappy that she cries often or doesn't bother to eat or get out of bed?'

Some questions will be asked to confirm the presence of specific symptoms, their intensity or duration Others, which you may think are unrelated or have nothing to do with the problems that brought you to seek help, are to exclude the presence of conditions that afflict many adolescents (e.g. difficulties concentrating, impulsivity). It often happens that parents are so worried about one behaviour that they disregard other relevant symptoms. Some teenagers and parents can become frustrated by this thorough questioning but it is the sign of a good clinician and the information is essential to make an accurate evaluation.

You will also be asked about your child's strengths, how you have already tried to deal with her problems, previous treatments and how successful they were. Questions will be asked about both parents' families of origin, whether there is a history of family problems, mental illness, drug and alcohol use, or suicide. This is because some problems tend to run in families and knowing what happened in one generation may help to understand the problems of the next. A detailed history of the young person's development, from birth to the current time, including school history, is also necessary.

Your child will be asked similar questions, usually on her own. Most clinicians spend some time during the initial evaluation with parents and child separately, to discuss matters that may be too sensitive to mention with the other family members present.

You will not be alone if you feel uncomfortable during these interviews. Most parents do, at least initially. Thoughts such as

'What have I done wrong with my child?' 'What is she implying by asking this?' cross their minds continuously. Because people feel anxious and stressed in these situations, they tend to become suspicious and misinterpret things. It is the rule rather than the exception to feel judged, threatened and criticised.

> *It is quite normal to feel tense, judged and guilty during interviews.*

To make things worse, you may also feel stupid if you can't remember when your child began walking, or said her first words, or other such details. When that happens, remember that no one in the room is judging you, they are just trying to help your child. These feelings usually disappear quickly, as soon as you get to know the clinician a little.

Spare a thought for your child. She usually feels much worse than you do. She's in the hot seat and everyone is actually talking about her, about what she does and feels in minute detail.

Don't feel embarrassed if your child, your spouse or your child's teacher disagrees with your opinion. This does not mean that any of them are being untruthful (although that can happen). Every person sees things from a different perspective and in a different context. Your husband, for example, may not believe you when you tell him about the battles you have with your child every evening about homework. When he arrives home from work, usually late in the evening, she is quite settled, watching television. On the other hand, you don't see what goes on in the classroom: teachers can observe that at first-hand. Also, teachers can compare your child's conduct with the behaviour of other children of her age and note differences more clearly. Finally, only your child really knows how she feels and what motivates her to do what she does, whether she can put it into words or not. To obtain an accurate picture it is essential to hear everyone's views.

As you may appreciate from the amount of information required, the initial assessment may take more than one hour, or it may take two or three sessions. On occasions this process brings to the surface old hurts, fears or sadness which had been left in unused corners of your mind because you have been to busy to even think about them. It can be quite healing too.

Investigations

Special tests might be required to clarify specific issues. The more commonly used tests are questionnaires, psychometric tests and achievement tests. Questionnaires are completed by adolescents, parents and teachers. They provide additional information to measure the extent and severity of problems from the perspectives of the adolescent, parents and teachers, and they are particularly useful in assessing progress in an objective way. Psychometric tests measure the teenager's intellectual ability and achievement tests estimate academic performance in a variety of subjects. These tests ascertain whether the teenager is performing at the level of her abilities.

Other tests may include electroencephalograms, computerised scans of the head and blood tests. In some cases a full physical or neurological examination may be required, and referral to a physician made for that purpose.

The clinician will discuss with you the reasons for the investigations and the cost, and will help to arrange them as well as explain the results.

RESULTS OF ASSESSMENT

At the end of the assessment the clinician should tell you whether there is a problem and, if so:

- which problems or disorders are present
- what caused or maintained these problems
- what the potential short- and long-term effects are for your child if she is left untreated
- **what treatments are available and for each one:**
  - the effectiveness
  - the risks
  - the side effects
  - how long will it take to work
  - the cost.

Feedback

At the end of the assessment process clinicians should give you their opinion and recommendations. This may require one or more sessions. It may entail meeting with you and your child together or separately and it is essential that you ask as many questions as necessary until you understand all the points.

It is normal practice for a consultant to inform the agency or professional (e.g. school counsellor, family physician) who made the initial referral of the results of the evaluation and recommendations. If you do not want that to happen, you should inform the consultant.

Treatment

This chapter describes how we know whether a treatment actually works and the different treatments available for adolescent disorders. They include individual psychotherapy, behavioural treatments, group therapy, family therapy and medication, as well as in-patient, residential and day treatment. Risks and precautions are also described.

The most important stage after the assessment is setting up and implementing a treatment plan. More often than not problems are complex. Clinicians, after discussion with the parents and the teenager, will set priorities to address some problems first and others later. Sometimes this will mean starting with the most harmful behaviour. For example, if your child is acutely suicidal, taking steps to ensure his safety would be the first priority. On other occasions it will mean beginning with something that is easy to achieve. Reaching a goal, even a small one, will make everyone more positive and put them in a better frame of mind to attempt more difficult tasks.

> **Different problems require different treatments.**

Different problems will require different treatments. Although aspirin is a very effective medication for headaches, it should not be used for everything and you would feel suspicious of a doctor who prescribes aspirin no matter whether you have pneumonia, a skin rash or a tumour. Likewise, you should question the skills of a therapist who can only provide one type of treatment, unless such treatment is so specialised that you were specifically referred to receive it. For each condition or problem there are treatments that work and treatments that don't work. These will be described later in the book.

In the course of forty years I have consulted a wide range of experts in the hope of finding a solution to my nocturnal enuresis [bed wetting] ... Most of the GPs advised curtailment of drinking and methods of awakening in the night. The urologists performed various technical studies that showed no abnormalities. Alarm systems usually gave relief for a short period. Consultations with a naturopath and a homoeopathist yielded no benefits, and consequent disappointment resulted in new mental strain ... I consulted a psychologist who, although unable to find anything abnormal in my personality, advised Pavlov's method of adaptation: immediately after waking with a wet bed, I was to take a cold shower as punishment for the 'bad' behaviour. A urologist prescribed imipramine, despite its severe side effects including excessive sweating, dizziness, and a dry mouth. The psychiatrist used sandpit therapy to trace traumatic experiences in childhood: recognition and acceptance of precipitating experiences might, it was hoped, remove the cause of my enuresis. Two years of weekly sessions of 45 minutes had a major influence in my personality. Sandpit therapy, with its focus on the ego, changed me from a sociable to a self-centred individual. Again, the bed wetting was unaffected ... Over the years, the intrinsic difficulties of nocturnal enuresis have been compounded by the effects of unsuccessful treatments.

M.J. De Graaf, '40 years of being treated for nocturnal enuresis', *Lancet* 1992, vol. 340, pp. 957–8.

How do we know if a treatment is effective?

Almost nowhere else in the many fields of human endeavour have people inflicted more pain on fellow human beings than in the quest for health. For centuries people have been bled, starved, fattened up, exorcised, purged, given vile potions, had their organs removed and had a thousand other unpleasant or horrible things done to them because someone believed it might cure them. This is not something you find only in history books, it is happening now. Just think of the millions of dollars people spend on vitamins that go down the drain, literally. This is because vitamins, with a little help from the manufacturers, have taken the public's imagination. Many people think these substances will make them healthier, stronger or wiser but the evidence to support such beliefs is non-existent (except for the very rare cases of vitamin deficiencies observed in developed countries). At least taking vitamins is mostly harmless. The effects on the household finances, the environment or the country's balance of payments might not be so benign though.

Until the 1900s treatments were empirical. That is, physicians based their practice on the results of observations and experiments, not on knowing why this or that treatment did what it was supposed to do. An empirical treatment is a therapy believed to be effective in practice but the mechanism of its action is unknown.

This is not very different from what Dr Hippocrates probably did more than two thousand years ago. Imagine one of his illustrious patients, Mr Plato, coming to the surgery complaining of a bad headache. After examining him, Dr Hippocrates concludes that it is not serious. He takes a few of his herbs and prepares an infusion. Mr Plato takes it and shortly after, the headache is gone and Mr Plato informs Dr Hippocrates of the dramatic cure. Excited by the success, Dr Hippocrates tries the remedy in a few more of his patients who come complaining of headaches. Many report relief. He then goes to the patent office and patents this tisane as a treatment for headaches. Because of Dr Hippocrates' fame and authority, many other doctors begin using it.

This *empirical* treatment for headaches was adopted because it was found (or believed) to have been successful in practice. The reason for its presumed efficacy, however, was unknown.

The placebo effect

What Dr Hippocrates did not consider is that if a doctor prescribes headache capsules containing sugar or water, or any other inactive substance, about four out of ten people will report relief of their pain. This is called the placebo effect. The inactive substance given as if it were a medicine is a *placebo*.

The simple act of taking a medication seems to make many people feel better. The extent of this effect varies depending on the treatment and the symptom. No matter what sick people do (take a remedy, jog, read tea leaves, diet, pray) someone is bound to get better some time. Clinicians and others who witness such improvements often attribute the cure to the *specific* effects of a treatment, when it may have had nothing to do with it. The mechanisms underlying the placebo effect are not well known but illustrate the close relationship between mind and body.

The picture becomes even more complicated because all clinicians want to believe their treatment is helping their patients. No practitioner is a truly independent observer. Patients also contribute to the deception. Even if they do not feel better, they often say that they do ('yes, a little better, doctor') because they want to be 'good' patients and not disappoint the doctor.

The result is that a multitude of treatments believed by doctors across the ages to be effective were in fact useless, if not harmful. If this is true in the domain of physical health, it is much more so in mental health where there are fewer objective measures. At least physical health has blood tests, thermometers and X-rays. Charlatans, clever operators who thrive on fashion, charismatic therapists and fanatics are more difficult to unmask. The solution for this problem is the controlled clinical trial.

> *Controlled clinical trials are the only way of proving the efficacy of most treatments.*

The controlled trial

A controlled trial requires administering the actual treatment or a placebo to two separate groups of patients and comparing the results between the two groups. Controlled trials are 'double blind' because neither the researcher nor the participants know who is receiving the treatment and who is getting the placebo. This prevents enthusiastic scientists deceiving themselves to come up with the results they want.

It is the practice in most countries not to license a drug for sale as a treatment for a condition until its effectiveness and safety have been proved in controlled clinical trials (this requirement does not apply to herbal remedies or dietary supplements). This is done to protect patients, often desperate to find a cure, who can become easy prey to unscrupulous practitioners or manufacturers. The latter are often helped by sensational and ill-informed, if not misleading, media reports. How many times have you read of claims for a cure for cancer, AIDS or other serious illnesses that came to nothing?

Controlled trials are particularly important in the case of mental disorders, which are largely subjective, have complex causes and subtle manifestations. They are easier to set up for medications (there are now controlled trials for most drug treatments used in psychiatry) but should also be used with every form of treatment, such as psychotherapy and family therapy. The results of these trials should guide clinical practice. This is called 'evidence-based practice'. It might be that many things taken for granted are just beliefs and have nothing to do with reality — for many centuries people were convinced that the earth was flat. Parents should ask clinicians treating their child about evidence for the effectiveness of the treatments they recommend.

Treating adolescents

There is a critical advantage in treating teenagers: they are in a state of change and development. If this is channelled in the right direction, it can produce outstanding results. This happens less often with adults, who are more set in their ways. In many cases, treatment will aim to help the natural process of maturation.

There are a variety of treatments that are effective in helping adolescents overcome their problems. The more widely used, either alone or in combination, are psychotherapy, cognitive-behaviour therapy, group therapy, family therapy and medication. They are usually administered at the therapist's office but can also be delivered in hospital or at home.

Individual psychotherapy

Psychotherapy is a term that can be applied to all treatments in which talking and listening are the main forms of intervention. An essential element of this treatment is the development of a therapeutic relationship between the adolescent and the therapist. Such a relationship will facilitate trust and help teenagers express their thoughts and feelings. The therapeutic relationship is different from an everyday relationship in that it takes place in a professional context and has rules and obvious boundaries. For example, it precludes a romantic involvement.

Typically, therapist and patient get together regularly, for a set period of time, and discuss thoughts, feelings and concerns. This may help teenagers become aware of the meaning of what they do or feel. With the assistance of the therapist, they can do something to change their behaviour and emotions.

There are many types of psychotherapy, each based on a different theory of personality and mental disorder. Counselling and psychoanalysis are forms of psychotherapy. However, every treatment involves a degree of psychotherapy as well as human warmth and understanding. The latter might be the most important element of all.

There is a myth that 'knowing' or 'getting to the bottom of it' will solve problems. Although this can happen in some unusual cases, it is not like that for the majority of cases. Knowing what is wrong and why is a good starting point, but it is only that. This is because once something begins to happen, it can quickly take on a life of its own and become established, a habit, part of life. It may be that you smoke or smoked in the past. You might have begun smoking because it was 'cool', because of peer pressure or for many other reasons. However, knowing why you began smoking will not make it any easier when you try to stop. Therapy requires effort to be effective.

Nigel was 13 and an only child. He had been referred for treatment because of stealing at school. Nigel had also been disobedient at home and at school, and he had run away from home overnight. This troubled period happened after the separation of his grandparents a few months earlier. They had looked after Nigel when he was younger and he was very attached to them. Separation also involved the relocation of his grandmother, who suffered from schizophrenia, and his 14-year-old uncle whom Nigel regarded as a brother.

It became clear after the first two therapy sessions that Nigel was unable to express his feelings of loss and was afraid that he would inherit his grandmother's condition. He released the tension and anger he felt through clashes with his parents and teachers, and acts of daring with peers.

In order to understand the meaning of these losses, Nigel, who had been suspended from school, was asked to spend time at home drawing pictures about the family. At the following sessions these drawings were discussed with his parents, who expressed feelings of loss and distress. Nigel also discussed these feelings and the therapist reassured him that he was not 'crazy'. The next step was to focus on his answering back when told to do something. His parents were asked to observe how they handled Nigel's argumentativeness.

By the next session, his parents had arranged for Nigel to spend some time with his grandmother and uncle in recognition of the importance of their relationship. Nigel's mother had become aware of her contribution to the problems by over-reacting to any sign of resistance. She spontaneously changed the way she asked Nigel to do things. Nigel was transferred to a new school to give him a fresh start. A few months later problems had not recurred.

Parents should be involved in the treatment. They should meet from time to time with the clinician treating their child or, in some cases, with another therapist. These sessions are important in several ways. On the one hand parents can inform the therapist about improvements (or worsening) in their adolescent's behaviour. Therapists can't just rely on teenagers' accounts or they will easily be taken for a ride. On the other hand, clinicians can give support to parents and help them understand their child's difficulties. Also, therapists can guide parents on practical ways of dealing with the special needs of their child.

Cognitive-behavioural treatments

Cognitive-behavioural treatments are a special type of more active psychotherapy, and they usually focus on specific problems. They are effective in conduct problems, depression and anxiety. The basic assumption is that if someone continues doing something, it is because what they are doing is being reinforced in some way. The reinforcement, or reward, keeps the behaviour happening. For example, you smoke another cigarette because the lack of nicotine in the brain makes you *feel edgy and uncomfortable*. Smoking raises the nicotine level in your brain and that gets rid of the unpleasant feeling so that you *feel better*. This *reinforces* your smoking. A child throws a tantrum in the shopping centre because he wants a sweet. The parent feels embarrassed and, after a short struggle, relents and buys him the sweet (reinforcement). The child learns that if he throws a tantrum in the shopping centre he gets what he wants. Although these explanations are simplistic, they summarise the theoretical basis of these treatments. In the case of smoking there is also an element of chemical dependency.

Everyone uses behavioural principles intuitively in everyday life. Your child does something nice such as offering you a cup of tea. If you praise him and show your appreciation, you are reinforcing that behaviour and increasing the chances that he will offer you a cup of tea another day. Being liked by your peers or by the people you value is one of the strongest reinforcers, particularly during adolescence.

Behavioural treatments have two main objectives. One is to find and apply reinforcers to develop a specific behaviour that is lacking. The other is to remove reinforcers that elicit or maintain undesirable habits. For example, your child does not make his bed and you want him to make it. You can negotiate with him that you will put a dollar in a jar every day he makes his bed, and take one out if he does not. If there is no money in the jar and he does not make his bed you will reduce his pocket money by one dollar. He is then allowed to spend any money left after one month. Money is a very strong reinforcer.

Cognitive treatments are based on the premise that our thinking, the way we perceive events and situations, influences our feelings and behaviour. For example, Anna was hoping for a phone call from her school friend Jenny to arrange to go to the movies. The call did not eventuate. Anna began thinking that Jenny no longer liked her because she was uninteresting and dull, that all her friends would probably ignore her in the future and that the group would reject her. These thoughts made Anna feel increasingly despondent. The reality was that Jenny had not been able to phone because her parents had asked her to do something else. Adolescents with depression, anxiety and other problems have distorted ways of thinking that reinforce their negative emotions.

In cognitive therapy, the clinician is like a coach, helping teenagers to:

- discover the link between their thoughts and feelings ('I am dull and boring, no good. This thought makes me feel sad.')
- identify negative habits of thinking ('Jenny did not phone. This means she finds me uninteresting.' 'No one will ever like me.')
- examine other plausible explanations for events or situations ('It may be that Jenny had something else to do, or forgot, or her phone was out of order, or she became ill.')
- recall occasions when something positive actually happened ('Yesterday Jenny said she enjoyed the game of tennis we played.')
- find proactive ways to avoid sinking into negative thinking ('I will phone Jenny to find out what is happening.').

These treatments appear simple but are not. Finding out what makes each person 'tick', what elicits what behaviour, and setting up or removing effective reinforcers requires an analytical mind, a good knowledge of the person, a high degree of skill and quite a lot of time and patience.

Behaviour treatments are more active, hands on. They involve tasks that need to be done at home, at school or in other real-life situations in which the adolescent's undesirable habits, fears or compulsions actually occur. When done well they can be very effective.

You may recall Bruce's case from Chapter 3. After much thought and with some trepidation, Bruce's parents asked the advice of their family doctor. They hardly knew her because the family had seldom been ill. She agreed with them that Bruce's behaviour was of concern and that he might have an emotional disorder. She recommended a consultation with a child psychiatrist to whom she had referred children with similar problems in the past with good results. The parents almost freaked out. 'A ... psychiatrist? God help us! Bruce is going insane', they thought. The physician, who noticed their alarm, reassured them that most people with psychological problems were not mad and that these behaviours were not rare.

In spite of their anxiety and the difficulties they had convincing Bruce of the need for the consultation, the visit to the psychiatrist was less painful than expected. They felt relieved to talk to someone who actually understood the situation. He seemed to anticipate their thoughts and through his questions they became aware of many little details in Bruce's behaviour that they had not thought unusual but that were part of the same pattern. Although initially reticent, Bruce also warmed up through the interview. The parents were surprised to hear how upset Bruce was by his own worries and how widespread these were. The psychiatrist told them that Bruce suffered from an illness called obsessive compulsive disorder. Treatment would entail several sessions with Bruce and them, some tasks to carry out at home and, probably, medication. With this treatment it was likely that Bruce would overcome this problem completely.

Treatment was quite intensive and went on for several weeks. Bruce and his parents learned to detect his worrying thoughts and the actions that he felt compelled to do to reduce his worry, and his parents learned that they should resist his attempts to do things his own way. Frequently they felt pangs of guilt when they realised that they had made things worse by adapting to Bruce's unreasonable requests.

Three months later Bruce was discharged from treatment. His behaviour had normalised and he was coping much better with school work. He had resumed going out with friends and was even showing a healthy interest in girls. His parents felt a great weight off their shoulders and the whole atmosphere in the house had changed.

Group therapy

As the name suggests, this treatment takes place in a group setting. It usually comprises six to twelve adolescents with similar problems who get together regularly under the guidance of a therapist or group leader. The objectives vary from improving social skills (by learning how to relate to peers and receiving their comments), to education, companionship and support.

This form of treatment can be particularly effective for adolescents, who are often more willing to reveal their thoughts or feelings to people their own age than to adults. Comments or observations by peers attending the group can be more powerful in changing their behaviour than parents' or a therapist's advice. It is less expensive than other therapy too. There is good evidence that group therapy is effective for anxious and depressed adolescents.

Although it is often used for them, group therapy is risky for teenagers with conduct, delinquent or drug-use problems as peer interactions outside the group are more likely to reinforce the disturbed behaviour. This usually outweighs the possible benefits of what happens during the group session.

Family therapy

Look at the room around you. Over time, the pieces of furniture and furnishings have found their place, and you have become accustomed to it. The balance has become familiar. Now, change the position of a sofa or a table, or paint the walls a different colour. The result is that everything looks and feels wrong, dislocated: that change has disturbed the harmony. To restore harmony you will need to rearrange the other pieces of furniture or change the colour scheme. Something similar happens in families. Changes in one family member, whether due to a psychological problem, treatment, circumstances of everyday life, or just growing up, result in changes in other family members and their relationships. Sometimes they are imperceptible, at other times they can be quite dramatic (remember the case of Karen in Chapter 2?). This is very noticeable when a new person comes into the family, for example when a child is born.

> *Treating adolescents without considering the persons with whom they live is likely to give poor results.*

Adolescents' problems usually generate a variety of responses from family members. These can range from self-blame to blaming others; from denial of responsibility to depression; from over-indulgence to severe criticism; from withdrawal to overinvolvement; from anger and excessive punishment to lack of discipline; from underestimating to overestimating the young person's symptoms or resources. Responses can be helpful or can make things worse. The younger the teenager, the more important is the involvement of the family in treatment.

Involving family members as a group in treatment is called *family therapy*. Such involvement may be informal or irregular, or formal and regular. Family therapy may be the main form of treatment or it can be used in combination with other therapies (remember that different problems, or different aspects of a problem, require different treatments).

The objectives of family therapy vary widely depending on the family and the type of problem. In some cases the main goal will be to inform family members about the characteristics of the adolescent's condition and how to manage or respond to it best. On occasion it will aim at exchanging information between the family and the therapist. Sometimes it will attempt to change unhealthy interactions between family members as these may cause or maintain the teenager's problems. Whatever the goals of the treatment, they should be spelled out and agreed upon early in the treatment process.

Medication

Medication has a limited but important part in the treatment of emotional and behavioural problems in adolescents. Drugs should not be prescribed in isolation, but as part of a treatment package that includes education on their use and other forms of therapy.

The medications used for the treatment of mental disorders are called *psychoactive* or *psychotropic* drugs. These are chemical substances that can modify feelings, abilities or behaviour. We all use psychoactive substances in our everyday life when we eat chocolate, or drink coffee, tea or wine. There are also psychoactive substances that can be abused because of the feelings of well-being they induce (most of them are illegal). Specific treatments involving medication are described in the chapters that follow.

Psychotropic medications should be prescribed and monitored by a doctor who is knowledgeable about the indications, dose, risks and side effects. Never administer one of these medications to your child because you, or some other relative, took it and found it helpful or because it was recommended by a friend or an acquaintance. This is because most medications can have unwanted side effects or be toxic.

Side effects, when they occur, appear at the dose required to obtain the therapeutic benefit and are an inconvenience that often has to be endured. They are usually mild. If they become troublesome, you should consult your doctor. When side effects become intolerable a change of medication may be required.

Toxic effects tend to be more severe and can even cause death. They typically occur when the adolescent takes an overdose, but in some rare instances can appear at normal or low doses because of an allergic reaction or because the teenager is taking another medication as well. Taking several drugs at the same time can result in interactions and may increase (or decrease) their respective effects. Taking several concurrent medications should be avoided. Psychiatric drugs often boost the effects of alcohol. Teenagers should avoid drinking alcohol while taking these medicines.

FREQUENTLY USED MEDICATIONS

The most frequently used medications are:
- those that increase concentration and reduce restlessness
- antidepressants
- those that decrease obsessive thinking
- sedatives
- those that help strange ideas or perceptions wane
- those that stabilise mood swings.

Names of drugs

Sometimes people become anxious because the name of the drug in the prescription (e.g. *fluoxetine*) is different from that on the container they get from the pharmacy (e.g. *Prozac*®). Typically, a medication has two names: a generic name and a proprietary name. The generic name (*fluoxetine*) reflects the chemical composition of the drug and is often long and difficult to pronounce. The brand or proprietary name (*Prozac*®) is chosen by the pharmaceutical company marketing the drug. It is usually short and catchy. The same drug may have several brand names if more than one manufacturer makes it. These names often carry the superscript ® to show that it is a registered trade name.

In-patient hospitalisation and residential treatment

The least restrictive form of treatment should always be used, particularly with children and adolescents, as there are risks involved in living in institutions and becoming used to a lifestyle that is very different from real life. Institutional living interferes with the development of autonomy, self-image and independence, and adolescents also lose contact with family and friends. Therefore, out-patient treatment is preferred to day-patient, and day-patient to in-patient, whenever possible.

In fact, there are few conditions that *require* hospitalisation. An ideal service should provide acute admission, longer-term in-patient, day-patient and out-patient treatment.

Acute in-patient treatment

Acute in-patient treatment is typically restricted to grave situations: circumstances in which adolescents are so disturbed that they require round-the-clock medical or nursing care and supervision. It can be involuntary. However, keeping teenagers in hospital against their will, particularly if they are older than 14 years, is subject to legal requirements (these vary according to state and country).

The main aims of acute hospitalisation are to protect teenagers or other people from the consequences of their disturbed behaviour, and to begin treatment (often with medication). Usually it is short-term: a few days, or two or three weeks. Teenagers are transferred to a less restrictive treatment setting as soon as possible.

Acute in-patient treatment may be necessary in cases of psychosis, severe depression or grave suicide risk. It might be warranted also in crisis situations. However, there are few facilities that specialise in the acute treatment of adolescents, so that they are often admitted to paediatric wards or adult units. Although not the best alternative, this is not necessarily harmful if these units are run properly.

Residential treatment

Other in-patient services, called 'residential', offer subacute treatment and rehabilitation programs. These are longer-term (three months or so) and treat less acute disorders, or continue treatment and rehabilitation of adolescents with an acute disorder once symptoms have become less severe. This may be necessary if other forms of treatment have failed and there is a good chance that in-patient treatment might succeed. Some of these facilities function Monday to Friday and teenagers go home on weekends.

Typically, acute in-patient and residential services are staffed by multi-disciplinary teams and offer a variety of concurrent treatments tailored to meet the needs of the teenager. These comprise:

• individual therapy
• group therapy
• behavioural treatment
• milieu therapy
• medication (if appropriate)
• educational programs.

Milieu therapy draws on the total environment of the unit; the expectations of the staff are consistent, there are rewards for appropriate behaviour, all staff members deal with conflict in similar ways, and there is a timetable that provides opportunities for peer interaction and development of social skills.

Some form of schooling is a necessary element in these facilities. Learning programs are essential to allow adolescents to continue their education.

> **In-patient admission is not risk-free.**

You should be aware, however, that in-patient admission is not without risks, despite staff's care and watchful eyes. Some young people are vulnerable to the influence of other disturbed teenagers and can become worse, at least temporarily. For example, they may start carrying out self-destructive behaviours (e.g. wrist slashing) to imitate or support similar acts by new-found friends. Others may embrace values alien to the family, become more rebellious at home, begin to smoke or develop unwelcome habits such as swearing.

Adolescents with problems of conduct (e.g. stealing, truancy, aggressive behaviour) or drug problems are seldom admitted to these programs, with the exception of short admissions in crisis situations. They require a more structured environment and longer treatment. Also, they should not be placed with teenagers with emotional disorders, as they often victimise them. These young people can be treated in smaller, specialised, long-term programs. Some non-government organisations and charities run facilities of this kind (e.g. Boystown).

Day treatment

Day treatment programs have the same characteristics as those described for residential settings. The only difference is that adolescents go home at night after having spent the day attending the program. The main shortcoming is that treatment facilities need to be at a reasonably short travelling distance from the teenager's home.

Assessing treatment effectiveness

Once treatment begins it is essential to monitor whether it is effective. This is routinely done by estimating the reduction in symptoms (e.g. a decrease in feelings of depression) and improvement in the adolescent's level of functioning at home and school (e.g. he is less irritable, participates more in family activities, is more motivated to do school work and more able to concentrate). Some clinicians use rating scales to measure the amount of change in the different areas and to track progress in an objective manner.

REASONS WHY A TREATMENT MAY NOT BE EFFECTIVE

- **It is the right treatment but the adolescent does not respond to or cooperate with it.**
- **It is the right treatment but it is not well administered:**
  - the clinician lacks the skills to give this treatment properly
  - the amount, or dose, is incorrect
  - the treatment not administered or taken for long enough.
- **It is the wrong treatment:**
  - it is not effective for this condition
  - it is effective for the condition but diagnosis is incorrect.

Treatment may not be effective for a variety of reasons. Not every individual responds to a treatment, even those that are normally very effective. It does not make sense to stick with a treatment that is not producing results. A competent professional will continuously monitor progress and reassess the situation if symptoms do not improve after an appropriate period. This may result in a change of treatment, a reappraisal or change of diagnosis or, if doubts persist, in seeking a second opinion. However, too many changes of treatment too soon are likely to be counterproductive. Treatments need to be given a chance to work and this requires time.

Poor compliance with treatment is a common reason for not achieving the expected results.

A frequent reason for failing to achieve the desired results is that adolescents (or families, in the case of family therapy) do not adhere to treatment. For instance, a teenager may appear to swallow the tablet but actually put it under his tongue and spit it out later. The same problems can arise with non-drug treatments. The teenager may fail to carry out instructions or exercises agreed to with the therapist. Non-compliance happens more often when teenagers are unhappy about the treatment or clinicians' demands are unrealistic. Trust and open discussion are essential to avoid this. Treatment regimes that are too complicated (for instance, having to take tablets three or four times a day) are also likely to result in poor compliance just because young people forget them. Keeping things simple is very important.

Because *all* treatments, not just medication, have risks and unwanted effects, are expensive and can require a considerable investment in time, a decision to undertake treatment should not be made lightly.

Depression

6

This chapter takes you through the detection, causes and treatment of clinical depression. You will learn how to know if your child suffers from depression, the difficulties adolescents with depressive illness and their families experience and what you can do to help your depressed teenager.

> In sooth, I know not why I am so sad:
> It wearies me; you say it wearies you;
> But how I caught it, found it, or came by it,
> What stuff 'tis made of, whereof it is born,
> I am to learn;
> And such a want-wit sadness makes of me,
> That I have much ado to know myself.
>
> William Shakespeare, *The Merchant of Venice*, act 1, scene 1, lines 1–7.

Sadness and unhappiness are a component of normal human experience. Sometimes, however, these feelings are so intense and persistent that individuals are unable to function at the level to which they are accustomed. It is in these situations that we talk of clinical depression, major depression, depressive illness or melancholia. People in everyday life speak about being 'depressed', meaning that they feel unhappy, down or sad. However, when I talk about depression I mean clinical depression.

Depressive illness is one of the most commonplace but obnoxious of human scourges. One in four women and one in eight men will experience an episode of clinical depression in their lifetime. No doubt you know some of them. The majority do not seek help, and will go on untreated because they think depression is part and parcel of life: 'the black dog' as Churchill used to call it. Because it can't be seen under the microscope or shown up by X-rays they do not consider it an ailment that can be treated, just something to be endured.

Depression is an impostor. An enemy who creeps in under false pretences, without being noticed. Little by little it takes you over. It gradually changes the way you think, feel, react, the way you are. It drains your energy and your illusions. It makes you believe there is no hope, that death would be a relief, a liberation. You become someone different. And you still think it is you!

> *Depression is not a weakness.*
> *It is a medical illness.*
> *Depression is treatable.*

Apart from the pain and misery it causes to the sufferer, depression also torments family and friends. Depressed people become sick more often, their marriages break up more often, they have lower paid jobs, go to the doctor more and die younger than those who do not have depression. Nobody likes depressed people because they are not fun to be with. It is a very serious problem and, what is even worse, seems to be on the increase in the young.

What is depression?

Imagine you are in an air-conditioned room. The temperature is pleasant and you feel comfortable and can work well. Probably the thermostat, the device that controls the air-conditioner and ensures a fairly constant temperature, is set at 18 or 20°C. However, if the thermostat breaks down and sets the temperature very low, say at 4°, you would be freezing. You would feel very uncomfortable, be shivering and unable to work. This is similar to what happens when you are depressed.

We all have a thermostat-like mechanism in our brain that controls our mood. As a result, our feelings oscillate within a normal range: we can feel happy or even very happy for a time when something good happens; we can also feel down for a period as a response to unpleasant situations. These fluctuations don't last long and we ordinarily return to a steady mood after a short while. People become depressed when this mechanism breaks down. When that happens the 'mood thermostat' sets the emotional temperature at very low levels, making us think, feel and react in a negative, hopeless way. It is as if, without realising it, you wake up one morning wearing dark-coloured glasses. Everything you see is grey, dark and gloomy. Many people in this situation think *they* are wrong, when in fact what is wrong is something that is *happening to them*.

This is one explanation of the mechanism underlying depression. There are many theories and some scientists believe there may be several types of depression. What is clear is that clinical depression is not caused by weakness, laziness or lack of willpower. It is a medical condition that can be treated.

What causes depression?

It would be useful to know what causes depression. This would facilitate prevention and finding better treatments, but there is still much we don't know.

Depression runs in families. Having a parent or sibling who suffered from depression increases the odds for the average teenager from one in twenty to one in ten.

Females are more prone to clinical depression than males. Some of the reasons for this are mentioned later in this chapter. Childbirth also increases the risk (post-partum depression).

In some people, a depressive episode can happen when life is going well but in many instances it is brought on by a particular event or experience, for example:

- a loss, such as the death of a loved one
- a traumatic or stressful incident, such as abuse, chronic social deprivation or rejection
- a physical illness
- some medications
- drugs of abuse
- the presence of other mental health problems.

Depression in adolescence

Mrs Smith made it clear that she had come along to the interview with her daughter, Amy, to keep the school counsellor happy, not because she thought there was anything wrong with Amy, let alone that she needed psychiatric treatment: 'What Amy needs is someone to teach her how to make friends.' The school counsellor had been concerned about Amy for some time. She had observed her becoming increasingly withdrawn and isolated from her peers, her deteriorating academic performance, her tearfulness. Amy's English essays, the few times she handed them in, were full of unhappy, hopeless and gloomy themes, so much so that they seriously concerned the teacher.

Mrs Smith said that Amy had been a bright, outgoing child until a year earlier when she seemed to gradually lose interest in things, stopped going out and began watching television all the time ('You know what puberty is like.'). When not watching television she locked herself away in her room for hours on end. She had become thinner, but her mother thought this was due to her rapid growth and 'Amy has always been a picky eater'. Mrs Smith was not surprised by Amy's moods, her storming out of the room, her crankiness and tears: 'Blessed adolescence! We all went through it,' she said.

Amy was an only child. Her father had left before she could remember and had not been in touch since. 'A scoundrel', in her mother's words. Mrs Smith had lived with another man for a few years but 'it did not work out'. Amy had been her main companion, and Mrs Smith believed she was Amy's 'best friend'. Mrs Smith had been depressed on and off, and saw her family doctor for it. 'He prescribed sleeping pills when what I needed was counselling. I will not forgive him ... I have changed doctors since.'

Amy was a thin, well-developed 15-year-old girl. She was fashionably dressed, stared melancholically in front of her and had dark shadows under her eyes. She did not say much when her mother was present. When alone, she poured out her unhappiness and despair, which she blamed on her friends. She felt there was no future for her. She was ugly and no one liked her. She believed she had been deceived, betrayed and rejected by her friends ('I can't trust people any more') and spent sleepless nights brooding about it. Amy did not see any point in living and had thought often about ending it all.

Depressive illness afflicts about 10 per cent of teenage girls and 5 per cent of boys, although marked feelings of unhappiness are much more common. Depressive episodes are not frequent in childhood but increase rapidly after puberty, particularly in girls. Why this is so is most intriguing and a number of explanations have been proposed. There is little doubt that hormonal changes are one culprit. Others think that adolescents' new-found ability to think in abstract terms and to project their unhappiness into the future allows them to experience hopelessness, a central characteristic of depression. This makes them more vulnerable to this condition. It might be that the loss of the support provided by the family (which protects younger children from depressive feelings) as a consequence of the teenagers' search for independence also plays a role. Finally, society's demands, pressures and expectations (particularly of women), which increase markedly after puberty, may be relevant also.

Severity of depression

Not all depressions are of the same severity:

- A depression is *severe* if the teenager has most of the symptoms of depression and can't carry out the day-to-day activities previously performed.
- An adolescent with *moderate* depression shows many symptoms of depression but can still manage to do some activities but not as well or as easily as before.
- *Mild* depression is present if the teenager has the minimum number of symptoms and can still do the things normally required but with more effort than previously.
- In unusual instances the depression is so severe that the adolescent loses touch with reality and becomes psychotic – this is *psychotic depression*. The picture is then similar to other psychoses and is described in Chapter 13.

How do I know if my child is depressed?

The basic features of a depressive episode are summarised in the box on page 75. Depression in adolescents is not much different from that observed in adults. The key characteristic is a change in the adolescent's usual level of functioning, accompanied by depressed mood, or loss of interest and enjoyment in almost all activities.

Depressed adolescents look sad and unhappy. They also appear cranky, grouchy, irritable and short-tempered. The latter may be even more noticeable than the sadness. They may feel that no one loves or cares for them and identify themselves with rebel, anti-authority role models. Occasionally they feel empty, without feelings. Other teenagers complain of non-existent aches and pains and may end up going to the doctor repeatedly.

Almost always they feel worthless. They become too sensitive to comments, which they misinterpret in a negative way. Their self-esteem and self-confidence plummet. They talk about not being able to concentrate and of lack of motivation. Even thinking requires a lot of effort. Molehills become mountains. Refusal to go to school because it takes too much effort or because they can't cope with it is not uncommon. Often they withdraw to their room where they agonise over things or lie in bed for hours, all of this being out of character with their previous behaviour.

FEATURES OF A DEPRESSIVE EPISODE

Your adolescent child probably suffers from depression if he or she:

- has shown a marked change in character, a decline in school work and a changed relationship to family and friends
- appears unhappy, tearful, down in the dumps or complains of sadness or emptiness, or has lost interest or enjoyment in most activities and pastimes previously enjoyed
- **and at the same time has shown four of the following symptoms:**
  - a considerable change in appetite or weight
  - a change in sleeping pattern: can't sleep at night or sleeps too much
  - is restless, agitated (pacing, wringing hands) or is slowed down (spends hours staring in front, finds it hard to move)

- has lost a lot of energy, complains of feeling tired all the time
- feels worthless or complains of feeling inappropriately guilty ('everything is my fault', 'I am bad')
- can't think, concentrate or make decisions
- believes that life is not worth living, there is no future and she will be better off dead.

Changes in appetite or weight are frequent. In depressed adults it is more common to see weight loss but adolescents can have increased appetite and weight gain (and the latter makes them feel even worse about themselves). Often there is a change in sleeping pattern: sleeplessness or sleeping too much. Typically, they lie in bed awake for long periods, torturing themselves with their misfortune. These adolescents often think of dying, of suicide. In quite a few instances they attempt suicide or do reckless things, not caring for the consequences.

Most teenagers are moody and show some of these symptoms. You don't need to worry too much unless the symptoms appear together and persist most of the time for a period of several weeks. A depressive episode is more than just feeling blue or down. The box on page 77 shows a widely used adolescent depression rating scale.

What do I do next?

Some depressed adolescents seek relief from their distress by drinking alcohol or using other drugs.

If you think that your child has these symptoms, you should seek professional advice to confirm the diagnosis and receive treatment (see the steps outlined in Chapter 4). This may be easier said than done. Teenagers often feel threatened or frightened by the thought that what is happening to them is beyond their control, or that there is something wrong with their mind. They react by denying they have a problem.

A DEPRESSION SCALE[1] FOR ADOLESCENTS

Below is a list of the ways you might have felt or acted. Please tick (✓) how much you have felt like this during the past week.

During the past week	Not at all	A little	Some	A lot
1. *I was bothered by things that usually don't bother me*	0	1	2	3
2. *I did not feel like eating, I wasn't very hungry*	0	1	2	3
3. *I wasn't able to feel happy, even when my family and friends tried to help me feel better*	0	1	2	3
4. *I felt like I was as good as other kids*	3	2	1	0
5. *I felt like I couldn't pay attention to what I was doing*	0	1	2	3
6. *I felt down and unhappy*	0	1	2	3
7. *I felt like I was too tired to do things*	0	1	2	3
8. *I felt that something good was going to happen*	3	2	1	0
9. *I felt like things I did before didn't work out right*	0	1	2	3
10. *I felt scared*	0	1	2	3
11. *I did not sleep as well as I usually sleep*	0	1	2	3
12. *I was happy*	3	2	1	0
13. *I was more quiet than usual*	0	1	2	3
14. *I felt lonely, like I didn't have any friends*	0	1	2	3
15. *I felt like kids I know were not friendly or that they didn't want to be with me*	0	1	2	3
16. *I had a good time*	3	2	1	0
17. *I felt like crying*	0	1	2	3
18. *I felt sad*	0	1	2	3
19. *I felt people didn't like me*	0	1	2	3
20. *It was hard to get started doing things*	0	1	2	3

[1]Center for Epidemiological Studies Depression Scale for Children. Faulstich *et al. American Journal of Psychiatry*, 1986, vol. 143, pp. 1024–7.

Scoring information is given on page 79.

The very symptoms of depression get in the way of people – adults, too – seeking help. They believe there is no point, that no one can help. When that happens, some adolescents may seek relief from their distress by spending much more time with friends, drinking alcohol or smoking marijuana, although most teenagers who abuse alcohol or drugs are not depressed.

Depression clouds these people's ability to judge what is happening and diminishes their insight. They try to make sense of the sadness they experience by blaming it on circumstances ('It's because my nose is too big', 'I don't have any friends'), events ('my boyfriend left me', 'my grandfather died') or abstract, philosophical concerns ('people are so bad that there is no future for the world', 'humanity is being slowly poisoned by pollution'). Frequently, they blame their family. They dwell on past arguments or incidents, feeding their anger and unhappiness. In this situation the last thing they want to do is listen to their parents. Keep these things in mind and don't be too upset by your child's angry retorts. This is the depression talking.

If your teenager denies having a problem or refuses help, ask a friend, relative or teacher close to her to speak to her. A crisis, for example a suicide attempt, although unpleasant, sometimes provides the opportunity for the teenager to accept there is something really wrong and to welcome help.

If you are still unsure whether your child has a depression, the best thing is to observe her behaviour closely for a little while. Be careful, however, not to be conspicuous or intrusive, or to give her the impression she is being watched. Teenagers are very jealous of their personal space and privacy. You may keep an eye on her weight, sleep, ability to enjoy things and laugh. Having a discreet talk with a teacher who knows her well or with some of her friends can be very illuminating. You can ask general questions such as if they had noticed a recent change in her mood or behaviour.

A PARENTAL RATING SCALE TO RECOGNISE DEPRESSION

For each item that describes your child *during the past month*, please circle **2** if the item is *very true* or *often true* of your child. Circle **1** if the item is *somewhat* or *sometimes true* of your child. If the item is *not true* of your child, circle the **0**.

0	1	2	Confused or seems to be in a fog
0	1	2	Cries a lot
0	1	2	Deliberately harms self or attempts suicide
0	1	2	Fears going to school
0	1	2	Fears he/she might think or do something bad
0	1	2	Feels he/she has to be perfect
0	1	2	Feels worthless or inferior
0	1	2	Likes to be alone
0	1	2	Nightmares
0	1	2	Too fearful or anxious
0	1	2	Feels too guilty
0	1	2	Overtired
0	1	2	Headaches
0	1	2	Shy or timid
0	1	2	Sleeps more than most children during the day and/or night
0	1	2	Stares blankly
0	1	2	Talks about killing self
0	1	2	Trouble sleeping
0	1	2	Underactive, slow moving, or lacks energy
0	1	2	Unhappy, sad, or depressed
0	1	2	Withdrawn, doesn't get involved with others
0	1	2	Worrying

If you add the numbers you have selected and the sum is 20 or above, there is a strong possibility that your child has a depressed mood.

Rey J.M. and Morris–Yates A. Diagnostic accuracy in adolescents of several depression rating scales extracted from a general purpose behaviour checklist. *Journal of Affective Disorders*, 1992, vol.26, 7–16.

Rating scales can be useful in some instances. On page 77 there is a rating scale to be completed by the teenager and on this page one for parents. You obtain a score from the scale completed by your teenager by adding the numbers your child has selected. A score above 20 for males and 22 for females is suggestive of a depressed mood.

Because every depressed person is potentially suicidal, it would also be prudent to take the precautions described in Chapter 8. The child's safety should always be the primary consideration.

Should I read my child's diary?

No hard and fast rules can be given about reading your child's diary: you should use your judgment based on knowledge of your child. If possible, discuss it with your spouse before doing anything. You should never do this just for the sake of it or to satisfy your curiosity. Two competing needs are in the balance: your child's wish for privacy, and her safety. Her privacy should be respected if at all possible, but if you are really concerned about her safety, reading her diary may clarify the situation.

I'm not the child's parent, what should I do?

Teenagers often confide their feelings or worries to other people – teachers, friends, parents of friends, ministers of religion, youth workers – or those people notice that something is not right.

What should you do? It is important not to ignore what you notice. You can't shrug your shoulders thinking 'it's not my problem'. We all have a duty of care, particularly towards young people, and should take reasonable steps to help. The younger the teenager the more assertive you need to be. Steps may include telephoning or writing to the child's parents to make them aware of your concerns, speaking to the child to clarify whether she is feeling OK and to offer help, or contacting child protection services if you are seriously worried about her safety.

If you talk to the child and she wants to swear you to secrecy, don't agree. Explain that you will keep what she is telling you in confidence but only if this does not compromise her or someone else's safety. If her safety is not an issue, you should respect her request but encourage her to talk to her parents or to seek appropriate help (e.g. from her general practitioner).

Treatment

Most people with depression can be helped. Often, teenagers (and their parents) don't realise they are depressed and don't seek help. There are a variety of psychological and drug treatments that reduce symptoms and prevent recurrence, either alone or in combination.

Treatment ought to address all aspects of the problem and not just depressed mood. This will often require remedial education or tutoring if the illness has interfered with learning at school or resulted in frequent absences. Social skills training may be required if the adolescent has difficulties relating to peers, and so on. Depression is usually treated in three stages:

1. The aim of *acute treatment* is to reduce the symptoms until the teenager goes back to her normal self. Her safety is the main concern. Admission to hospital might be necessary if she is very ill, psychotic or acutely suicidal. Residential treatment can be useful in severe cases that have not responded to other forms of treatment. With these rare exceptions, most depressed adolescents can be treated as out-patients.

2. *Maintenance treatment* (the continuation of treatment for some time even if the teenager feels completely well) aims at preventing the depression from coming back. Ceasing treatment too early may result in a relapse. Also, some people have repeated episodes of depression every few months or years and they will require ongoing treatment.

3. *Prevention of recurrences* is the third stage. Because recurrences are so frequent, once teenagers have recovered it is important to put in place mechanisms to prevent recurrences and to detect them early.

Psychological treatments

Counselling, psychotherapy, cognitive behaviour therapy and family therapy can all be useful. The goals of these treatments are to:

- inform the teenager and her family about the condition
- relieve stressful or conflictive situations
- help to set up experiences that the teenager can enjoy and in which she can succeed
- teach the teenager how to develop more positive thinking
- help the teenager improve her ability to deal with friction in social situations
- provide support.

Cognitive behavioural treatments are particularly effective in preventing depression in teenagers at risk and for treating mild and moderate depression. This treatment was described in Chapter 5. If there is no improvement after four to six weeks, other treatments should be considered.

Antidepressant medications

Medication is not usually necessary for adolescents with mild depression, at least initially. There are three types of antidepressant drugs:

- The tricyclic antidepressants have been known for some time. I will refer to them as the 'old antidepressants'.
- The monoamino oxidase inhibitors are mostly not used for adolescents because of their risks and side effects. The exception is moclobemide (Aurorix®).
- The so-called 'selective serotonin reuptake inhibitors' (SSRIs) have been introduced in the last twenty years and I will call them the 'newer antidepressants'.

The *old antidepressants* are well known and have successfully treated depression in adults for many years. However, treatment trials with children and adolescents have failed to show they are better than a placebo. Because of this and because of their toxicity, particularly on overdose, the old antidepressants should be avoided, as depressed teenagers are particularly prone to taking drug overdoses. Old antidepressants also have uncomfortable side effects such as dry mouth, constipation, blurred vision, drowsiness and increased appetite. Always keep these drugs under lock and key.

The *newer antidepressants* are more effective in the treatment of depression in children and adolescents. Some of the brand names are Aropax®, Luvox®, Prozac® and Zoloft®. Apart from their effectiveness, the newer antidepressants are much safer than the old ones and have fewer side effects. The more common are nausea, diarrhoea, loss of appetite, insomnia and tiredness. There have been suggestions in the lay media that these drugs can increase the risk of suicide or violent aggression. In spite of the fact that they have been used very widely, there is no evidence of such effects, although in some cases they can cause nervousness and agitation.

Antidepressants take up to three weeks for effects to show. Therefore, it is important to be patient. You should not mix several antidepressants together with the hope of better or quicker results. The combination of an old and a newer antidepressant can be particularly dangerous. Also, you should inform the doctor if your teenager is taking other medications as drug interactions are common.

If depression benefits from medication, your child will need to continue taking antidepressants for six to twelve months. Stopping medication earlier can result in a relapse. When antidepressants are stopped, it should be done gradually over several weeks. Ceasing to take the medication suddenly can produce unpleasant symptoms such as nightmares, restlessness and agitation (withdrawal symptoms).

Lithium

Lithium is effective in preventing recurrence of depression in adolescents with bipolar disorders. It will be described in more detail in Chapter 7.

Electroconvulsive therapy (ECT)

Many people have strong negative views about ECT, often the result of its pejorative portrayal in movies such as *One Flew over the Cuckoo's Nest*. However, some adolescents who received this treatment found it less unpleasant than medication or depression itself.

ECT consists of the passage of an electric current through electrodes placed on the scalp. This produces a convulsion that has an antidepressant effect. A series of six to twelve of these treatments improves the mood in most severely depressed patients. The procedure has become much safer and more sophisticated since its initial description in the 1930s. Nowadays, it is performed under a light general anaesthetic and with a muscle relaxant that stops the muscle convulsion. ECT is a safe and effective treatment for depression. Although its use in the young is rare, it ought to be considered for seriously depressed adolescents who do not respond to other forms of treatment.

ST JOHN'S WORT, A NATURAL ANTIDEPRESSANT?

St John's wort (*Hypericum perforatum*), also known as hypericum, is a herbal remedy that has become very popular due to the belief that it is a natural, safer antidepressant. It is a small flowering plant native to Europe, Asia and Africa. European migrants introduced it to North America where it grows wild, particularly in Oregon and the Pacific Northwest. In Australia, it was introduced to the Ovens Valley in Victoria during a gold boom in the 1880s, when a German woman imported seed of the plant and established it for medicinal purposes. It soon overran her garden and spread, subsequently being declared a noxious weed.

St John's wort can be tried in adolescents with milder depression or when other treatments have failed or caused serious side effects, but always under the supervision of a physician. Contrary to the situation with most alternative treatments there is some research evidence about the efficacy of St John's wort in depression. However, there are no studies in children and adolescents. The mechanism of action is unknown.

St John's wort is widely available in health food stores or via the Internet, although the quality of the brands is often poor. Many preparations also have other ingredients and should be avoided. The adult dose is 300 mg of plant extract (standardised to 0.3 per cent hypericin) orally three times daily. If side effects are marked, or if there is no improvement after six to eight weeks, the herb can be stopped gradually and another treatment considered. It is advisable to wait two weeks after ceasing St John's wort before taking another antidepressant.

There is a widespread belief that 'mother nature' is nurturing and harmless, and so herbal treatments, being natural, are safe. This is not always so, but St John's wort is usually well tolerated. The most common side effects are nausea, allergic reactions, fatigue, restlessness and photosensitivity (a reaction of the skin when exposed to sunlight). However, St John's wort has potentially serious interactions with many prescribed medications, for example, the contraceptive pill (it can become ineffective), asthma medications and antidepressant drugs. Therefore, it is very important not to take St John's wort together with other prescription drugs. It is also advisable not to take the herb if you are pregnant (risk of miscarriage), not to sunbathe (photosensitivity), and to wear wrap-around sunglasses (possible risk of cataracts). Always tell your doctor if you are taking St John's wort.

What can I do to help with the treatment of my child?

Parents and carers play an essential role in treatment. Here are some things you can do to help with your child's treatment:

- Be hopeful – in the majority of cases the results are good.
- Get support from someone you trust, and regular rest and relaxation (this may require enlisting the help of relatives or friends to care for your teenager for a while). If you are working you may need to rearrange your working hours or commitments so that you are less pressured. It will be best for your child if you feel strong and relaxed; you won't be much help if you are exhausted and on edge. Remember, you are only human.
- Don't be impatient. Overcoming this problem is not a matter of days but weeks or months.
- Ask the doctor for specific directions on your role in the treatment.

- Keep the doctor informed of your child's changes, progress or side effects of medication.
- Follow the doctor's instructions. If you don't understand or disagree about something, ask for clarification or discuss it openly.
- Make realistic allowances for the effects of depression on your child, but don't allow her to be too dependent or to regress into the sick role. There are things she can do, even if they are simple and for short periods.
- Encourage her involvement in enjoyable activities (even if she does not seem to enjoy them much now) and contact with supportive friends.
- Be ready to listen but don't force her to talk.
- Give enough space but keep a watchful eye (particularly for suicidal behaviour).
- Try to reduce the overall level of stress or change in the family by postponing things that can be left for later on.
- Don't take her angry remarks personally: it is not your child who is speaking, it is her depression.
- Encourage your teenager to continue with treatment for as long as her doctor recommends, even if she is feeling better.

When Anna was admitted to the unit, she had been depressed for about a year. She had stopped seeing her friends and going out, her school work had dived, together with her concentration and motivation. If you did not know all this and you observed her in the corridor or the gardens talking with other patients you would have wondered why was she in hospital. She kept to herself but when she talked and gestured she did so with some vitality and charm, as most 17-year-olds do. If not bursting with laughter, she could certainly smile. Anna was not the image of sadness and despair you would have expected. However, despite her normal appearance, she had deep feelings of hopelessness and gloom, which she acknowledged openly when questioned. Anna's recurring thoughts of suicide concerned me most because several of her relatives had killed themselves. It was like a family tradition. Previous treatment with old antidepressants and counselling had not made any difference and that had been one of the reasons for her admission.

Neither I nor the rest of the team were much the wiser after observing Anna's behaviour and listening to her concerns for three weeks. There seemed to be no explanation for her depression. Subsequently, one of the newer antidepressants was tried and her mood steadily improved, although very gradually. She became more outspoken and somewhat aggressive and angry, but her sadness, her hopelessness and her ability to concentrate in her studies strikingly improved. Her thoughts of dying gradually vanished. Anna returned to her school two months later, and I heard some time after that she was doing well and was happy.

What happens when depression is not treated?

Depressive symptoms unfold gradually, during weeks or months. Once they are established, a depressive episode typically lasts between six and eight months. Two out of three adolescents will recover fully. They go back to what they were prior to the illness, although they may have to repeat a year of school or catch up with what they missed during the time they were depressed. Even if nothing is done except preventing complications, the medium-term outlook for most people is excellent.

One adolescent out of three continues to show depressive symptoms of more or less severity for longer periods, up to several years. During that time their life is impaired to a variable degree, depending on the severity of the depression. Symptoms become chronic in about 10 per cent of teenagers with major depression. (When depressive symptoms persist for more than twelve months but are not as severe as those of major depression, the condition is called *dysthymic disorder* or *dysthymia*.)

Depression is more like asthma than pneumonia.

Because in most cases this depressive episode will be the first one, predicting what will happen later on is particularly difficult. Past history is always the best predictor of the future. In general, about half of the young people who suffer a depressive episode will not have a recurrence. The other half will have further episodes. Of those who have two episodes, 70 per cent will have a third. That is, the probability of further episodes increases depending on the number of previous episodes. Teenagers who recover only partially are more likely to have further recurrences of the illness as well. Most people think of depression as an acute illness like pneumonia. This is not true. Depression is often a chronic recurrent illness like asthma. Long-term treatment and prevention of recurrences is paramount.

About 15 per cent of these adolescents will develop a bipolar disorder (manic depressive illness, see Chapter 7). The likelihood of this happening is higher if a family member has had bipolar disorder.

Some of the long-term consequences of depression have already been mentioned at the beginning of the chapter. About 15 per cent of individuals with severe depression will commit suicide in the future. Depression in adolescence may also result in school failure, cigarette smoking, abuse of alcohol or drugs and conduct problems. These can complicate the situation considerably.

As you can see, depression is not a mild condition that can be easily ignored. Early treatment is strongly advised.

Mood swings

7

The subject of this chapter is bipolar disorder, also called manic depressive illness, and you will learn about its manifestations and treatment. Because it is often chronic, with recurrent episodes, treatment with lithium as well as the difficulties usually encountered in maintenance treatment are described in some detail.

Teenagers are well known for their 'moods'. They can feel extremely happy one minute and be in the depths of despair the next, all for a minor disappointment or because something did not go their way. Thankfully, gloom does not usually last. A phone call from a friend or something similar and they are happy again, chatting away on the phone as if there was no tomorrow or no one else in the house. These changes of mood are normal in teenagers. The topic of this chapter is not these frequent, benign mood swings but a more malignant problem. Some people have terrible 'lows' (depressions) and 'highs' (mania) that last for weeks or months at a time. In between they may feel completely normal. This problem is technically called *bipolar disorder* or *manic depressive illness*.

Bipolar disorder is a serious illness in which medical treatment is very effective.

What is bipolar disorder?

Bipolar disorder is characterised either by manic episodes or by alternating manic and depressive episodes, also known as phases.

All you learned about depression in Chapter 6 can be applied to the depressed phase of bipolar disorder. In fact, a number of adolescents who present with depression actually suffer from bipolar disorder, but this might not have been detected at the time because depression was the first manifestation of the illness. Bipolar disorder becomes apparent only if that teenager has a manic episode later.

Bipolar disorder is usually a serious, chronic medical condition, in many ways similar to diabetes or asthma. Although not as frequent as depression, it is not a rare illness – one person in a hundred suffers from it. Symptoms often start during adolescence (manic episodes are very unusual before the age of 12 years) but can begin at any time. Unlike the case with depression, as many males as females suffer from bipolar disorder.

What is mania?

Everything you read about depression in Chapter 6 can be applied to a manic episode, with the difference that the mood is elevated. The thermostat-like mechanism that controls mood is abnormally set at a 'high' level (this is likely to be due to chemical changes in the brain). The resulting elation colours the way teenagers perceive themselves. They believe they are brilliant, rich, attractive – as unrealistic a perception as was the one they had when depressed.

PROMINENT PEOPLE WITH BIPOLAR DISORDER

Many historical figures and very accomplished people are believed to have suffered from bipolar disorder. These are some of them:

- Balzac
- Beethoven
- Winston Churchill
- Dickens
- Goethe
- Handel
- Hemingway
- Abraham Lincoln
- Newton
- Tolstoy

What causes bipolar disorder?

Bipolar disorder runs in families, even more so than depression, and having a parent or sibling with bipolar disorder increases the chances of suffering from this illness. About 15 per cent of adolescents with a major depression will eventually develop bipolar disorder. Hormonal changes are as important here as in depression; occasionally, women feel that their symptoms become worse before menstruation. The loss of a parent or a friend, conflicts and traumatic events can bring about a manic episode or a relapse in people predisposed to the illness.

Sometimes, treatment with antidepressant medication can cause manic symptoms. Usually these cease when medication is stopped. Some other medicines, physical illnesses and drugs of abuse can produce changes in behaviour very similar to those seen in mania and this is why a full medical history and a drug screen (blood tests to detect if the adolescent was under the effect of a drug) are required when assessing people with these symptoms.

FEATURES OF A MANIC EPISODE

An adolescent is likely to be having a manic episode if:

- he shows an abnormally elevated, expansive or irritable mood that is out of character with his previous personality and lasts a week or longer
- these symptoms cause problems at home, school or in relating to friends
- **and, simultaneously, he shows three or more of the following symptoms:**
    - grandiose ideas or inflated self-esteem
    - less need for sleep
    - can't stop talking or is much more talkative than usual
    - feels that his thoughts race inside his head all the time, or his speech is difficult to follow because he changes from one topic to another
    - is easily distracted and can't keep his attention on one topic
    - is much more active than usual
    - becomes excessively involved in pleasurable but risky activities with potentially damaging consequences (e.g. foolish sexual indiscretions, overspending).

How do I know if my child has a manic episode?

Manic symptoms are the opposite pole of depressive symptoms (hence the name bipolar). Where there was unhappiness there is elation. Feeling overconfident takes the place of despair. Frantic activity, endless ideas, boundless energy substitute for the lack of vitality and motivation seen in depression. Manic adolescents appear too cheerful, even euphoric. They lose their normal inhibitions and indiscriminately talk to strangers or become involved in risky, senseless sexual liaisons. Occasionally they become irritable, particularly if they are contradicted or if they can't do what they want.

If depression impairs judgment, elation does so even more. Manic adolescents may believe they have more financial resources than they actually have and go on spending sprees, or they may feel they are extremely attractive and go on binges of indiscriminate sex. They may think that they know how to 'make a killing' in the stock market and invest the family's money, which they lose. Imprudent decisions taken when judgment was impaired by the elevated mood can result in disaster for the adolescents, their health, their career, their family or relationships.

Manic teenagers sleep less and often decide to do things noisily in the small hours, waking up the rest of the family. They are loud, don't stop talking and their thoughts jump from one topic to another. You may initially find this funny or amusing but it soon becomes unpleasant and, with time, unbearable. Sometimes the pressure to talk is so great that their speech becomes incoherent. Ability to concentrate diminishes and they move from one unfinished task to another. Symptoms can become so intense that adolescents appear psychotic. Distinguishing bipolar disorder from schizophrenia is often difficult in this age group, even for experts. This is discussed in more detail in Chapter 13.

As in other disorders, these features represent a marked change from adolescents' previous conduct. Most teenagers with this condition find it difficult to relate to the family, perform at school or work, or to get along with friends.

Mark's parents' hearts sank when the police telephoned informing them that he had been taken to hospital in a disturbed state. They had been half expecting something like that to happen, and although they did not voice it, deep down they felt relieved. They had tried on many occasions to take him to a doctor, pleaded with him, threatened him and bribed him, all to no avail. Of late, he had become very angry and screamed at the mere suggestion of this. His parents were completely puzzled by the change. If that were adolescence, Mark's two older brothers and sister had not gone through anything like it.

Mark had been a sensitive, intelligent and shy boy, more so than his siblings, who preferred sports and rough-and-tumble play. He had inherited his mother's musical interests and was the apple of her eye. His problems began shortly after his sixteenth birthday. Later his parents cursed their initial satisfaction with what seemed to have been a very positive change. Mark had become more confident, went out with friends more and appeared happier. He was finally becoming like his siblings had been at his age.

The first sign that all was not well unfolded a few weeks later. To their disappointment, Mark announced that he had realised that his future was in modelling and acting, and that he was planning to leave school to pursue this career. 'If Mel Gibson could do it, so can I!' he used to say emphatically. He then spent the money he had carefully saved for a trip overseas on a portfolio of studio photographs. What followed was a week of endless activity, visiting modelling agencies and organising appointments. He did not stop to eat and slept only three or four hours each night. He seemed very happy, though. He joked, sometimes telling spicy stories that made his mother and sister blush (and that was not easy). He was also able to explain away his parents' concerns, at least for a few hours.

His parents' suspicions that something was not well were confirmed when Mark began telephoning Los Angeles in the middle of the night trying to get acting roles. He became very aggressive when his father told him the family could not afford the telephone bill and that he was to stop doing that. He seemed to become much worse after this incident.

It was more difficult to follow his ramblings and his endless chatter. Everyone's nerves were on edge and arguments became an everyday occurrence, so much so that Mark's eldest brother decided to leave 'this madhouse' and rent a flat with a friend. His mother felt that the family was falling apart.

The phone call came a few days later. Mark had wanted to board a plane to Los Angeles without a ticket. He was saying almost incoherently that Rupert Murdoch had promised him the lead role in a new movie and that 'Rupert will pay for the ticket'. Airport staff thought he was on drugs and called the police. The resident's opinion at the emergency ward was that Mark was psychotic, probably manic. Because Mark did not want to stay, an involuntary admission to the psychiatry unit was organised.

Severity of mania

The severity level varies considerably from person to person, from mild (when showing some symptoms and impairment) to severe (when symptoms and impairment are marked). Some teenagers show these symptoms for only very short periods, or symptoms are not serious enough to warrant a label of bipolar disorder because the adolescent is not *impaired* by them. When that happens, it is called a *hypomanic episode*. In the more severe cases, adolescents lose touch with reality and become psychotic.

What happens when mania is not treated?

Left to their own devices, manic episodes can last from a few weeks to a few months but are generally shorter than depressive episodes. Once the episode is over most adolescents return to their former self. This usually means going back to a changed situation, because they may have lost months of school, hurt relatives, alienated friends or squandered money. Coping and coming to terms with the aftermath of their behaviour while they were manic is a considerable task.

> *The majority of people who have had a manic episode go on to have more.*

This is not all, though. The majority of people who have had a manic episode go on to have more, the average being four episodes of mania or depression in ten years. In some people, episodes are separated by many years of completely normal life. One in five teenagers do not recover fully between episodes. Although not showing definite symptoms, their mood remains unstable, labile, and they continue having problems coping with school, work, family and friends. A small minority of adolescents with this disorder have four or more manic or depressive phases in one year. This is called *rapid-cycling*. Occasionally teenagers may show features of mania and features of depression alternating for short periods in the same day. These are called *mixed episodes*.

The pattern of episodes varies from person to person. Often this pattern is characteristic for a particular individual (e.g. a depressive phase immediately follows a manic episode) and repeats itself. The presence of only manic phases and no depressive phases is possible but uncommon.

> *On average, there is a gap of seven years between the time when symptoms first appear and the time treatment starts.*

Adolescents with this condition often abuse drugs and alcohol, become involved in antisocial or delinquent activities, fail at school and lose jobs. Suicide is also a serious risk during the phases of depression.

The unavoidable conclusion is that bipolar disorder is a serious medical illness that requires treatment as soon as possible. The good news is that there are very effective remedies to control it, although there is no 'cure'.

What can I do?

If you have a well-founded suspicion that your child has a manic episode, you should take him to see a psychiatrist as soon as possible. This is because the basic treatment is with medication. Early detection and treatment are essential to prevent the consequences of the illness, which are often worse than the illness itself. On average, there is a gap of seven years between the time when symptoms first appear and the time treatment starts, and seven years represent much suffering that could have been avoided.

The main hurdle you will face is convincing your child that he has a problem and that he needs treatment to overcome it. If this is difficult in depressed adolescents, it is a real challenge in manic ones. Depressed people suffer because of the depression and treatment can mean a relief from their torment. Manic teenagers, on the contrary, have a great time. They feel good. They are on an almost continuous high without taking drugs. Their mind is clearer, they have more energy, they feel better than ever. 'Why should I see a doctor to get rid of this wonderful feeling?' your child will probably say. Insight is often very limited during a manic episode.

You will need all the help you can gather from family and friends to convince your child of the need for treatment. Wait for the right time. Even insightless adolescents have insightful moments or times during which they become exhausted and may be more open to advice. Avoid direct confrontation. If you are not making headway, retreat. Shouting or threatening will only make things worse. Manic individuals are irritable and can become violent if provoked. Their normal self-control does not work well during these periods.

Discuss the situation with your family doctor when you become aware of the first signs. Find out if there is a psychiatrist who would be available to see your child at short notice and, if you can, discuss your predicament with him or her. You may also ask about services available in your area, particularly to deal with crises. Get in touch with support groups for people with relatives who have this condition. Their experiences will be most helpful.

Involuntary admission to hospital

If the condition has become so bad that the teenager, or the rest of the family, needs to be protected from his behaviour and everything else has failed, you can take him to the emergency room of a hospital and request an admission against his will. If the situation has reached that stage, two issues are important:

- First, you need to gather enough information to show that he is disturbed.
- Second, you will need to demonstrate that he is dangerous to himself (this would include harm to his good name or financial situation) or to other people.

It will not be enough to say that you don't want your child at home or that you can't control him. There are strict legal requirements about keeping people in hospital or treating them against their will. You will need to convince not only the hospital doctors of the gravity of the situation but also, in many situations, a magistrate. Although you may think this is just too hard, it is designed to avoid abuses.

Reports from friends, neighbours or teachers supporting your descriptions are very helpful. Don't underestimate your teenager's abilities. He will probably act during interviews with professionals as a reasonable person. He may deny having any problems and even blame you, or something else, for the 'misunderstandings' that resulted in his ending up in hospital. If the doctor is not convinced, the teenager may agree there is something wrong with him but bargain by saying he will take treatment only if he is allowed to go home.

In rare instances, such as in the case study presented above, manic teenagers become a public nuisance and the police deal with them, usually by taking them to hospital. If this happens, it is important that you provide as much information as possible to the doctors, to facilitate diagnosis and treatment.

These are worst-case scenarios that rarely happen. The situation will seldom reach that stage, particularly if you act early, but you need to be prepared for every eventuality. Such dramatic actions are upsetting for everyone. Guilt, shame, anger and frustration are feelings that most parents experience in similar circumstances. An involuntary admission should not be organised without having thought carefully about the pros and cons. However, if needed, it should be done quickly. Procrastination usually makes things worse.

Treatment

Treatment is very effective in reducing the severity of the acute phase and decreasing the recurrence of episodes, both manic and depressive. Although the person may be completely well, treatment might need to be lifelong to prevent new episodes. Management of this illness is complex and you will find here only a brief description of the main issues.

The broad goals of treatment are:

- to decrease the severity, frequency and consequences of acute episodes
- to improve functioning between episodes.

Acute episode

The first important decision is about the level of care required. Apart from cases in which adolescents will need hospitalisation for their own protection or the protection of others, most teenagers can be treated at home. However, a short in-patient stay is often advisable. This is particularly so during the first episode of the illness. Because of their lack of insight and disorganisation, most of these young people will be unable to carry out the treatment at home and will find it difficult to provide the necessary feedback to the specialist. Hospitalisation allows a closer monitoring of the illness and side effects, which are important during the first episode. Decision about the best treatment setting, however, will depend on how much the family can do and whether there is support from community health teams. For example, it may depend on whether there is a psychiatric service that has medical or nursing staff who can visit the child at home regularly and respond promptly to crises.

Medication

Treatment with medicines is critical, particularly in the acute phase. The generic names of the drugs shown to be effective are presented in the box on page 99.

MEDICATIONS FOR BIPOLAR DISORDER

Medications effective in the treatment of the manic phase of bipolar disorder are:

- **mood stabilisers**
  - lithium
  - valproate
  - carbamazepine
- **medications that reduce symptoms**
  - antipsychotic drugs (see Chapter 13)
  - benzodiazepines.

Medications effective in preventing new episodes are:

- lithium
- valproate
- carbamazepine.

Lithium carbonate is the most effective treatment of acute episodes. Its anti-manic properties were described by the Australian psychiatrist John Cade in 1949. Also, its risks and side effects are well known (see page 100). Recently valproate and carbamazepine, two drugs previously used in the treatment of epilepsy, have also been found to be effective. Electroconvulsive therapy (ECT) is very safe and effective but seldom used because of the stigma attached to it. Antipsychotics and benzodiazepines have a less specific effect, although they can be helpful during the initial stages of treatment by reducing agitation and sedating the adolescent. The treatment of the depressive phase is similar to that described in Chapter 6, with the difference that medication should be used earlier.

Prevention of recurrences

Because people with this condition, if not treated, will have on average four episodes in ten years, the matter of long-term prophylactic treatment needs to be considered. (A prophylactic treatment is one that tries to prevent a disease from developing.)

The young person, his parents and the psychiatrist will need to discuss this in detail.

Lithium is equally effective in preventing the manic and depressive phases of the disorder. Thanks to long-term lithium treatment many people whose lives had previously been disrupted by a succession of manic and depressive episodes are able to lead perfectly normal and productive lives. Both valproate and carbamazepine also appear to be effective.

Treatment with lithium

Lithium has a quite narrow range in which it is effective and safe: too low a dose and it does not produce results, too high and it becomes toxic. As a consequence, lithium treatment requires close medical supervision. This entails regular blood tests (initially weekly, later on monthly or every three or six months) to establish whether the level of lithium in the blood is within the therapeutic range, as well as close monitoring of side effects. The more frequent of these are shown in the box below.

COMMON SIDE EFFECTS OF LITHIUM

Common side effects of lithium are:

- fine tremor
- headaches
- weight gain
- thirst
- need to pass urine often
- bringing about or worsening acne
- stomach ache.

Common toxic symptoms of lithium are:

- marked tremor
- nausea
- vomiting
- blurred vision
- vertigo
- unsteady gait
- slurred speech
- disorientation or mental confusion.

Although side effects are common, they are usually mild and can be overcome by rearranging the dose or schedule. Lithium also has effects on the functioning of the thyroid gland in about 5 per cent of people. The thyroid gland produces a hormone that regulates the speed of the body's metabolism. Lithium can reduce the production of this hormone, resulting in hypothyroidism, but this can be easily fixed by taking thyroid hormone tablets. However, the doctor needs to check this from time to time. Women who are planning to become pregnant should not take lithium as it can cause deformities in the baby.

Toxic effects can be serious and need to be watched for constantly. If you notice that your child shows signs of toxicity, lithium should be stopped immediately. After that you should take him to the doctor, who will organise a blood test to measure the actual level of lithium in the blood. This will confirm if the symptoms were indeed a manifestation of toxicity or of something else, such as a gastric infection. If symptoms are serious or if you think the teenager might have taken an overdose, he should be taken to the emergency department of a hospital as soon as possible.

> *The potential problems faced during treatment with lithium are no worse than those faced by diabetics or asthmatics.*

Bowel infections that produce diarrhoea can result in an increase of the level of lithium in the blood. Other medications can also do that. You need to tell the doctor if your child is taking other medications, particularly diuretics or anti-inflammatory drugs. This also applies to herbal remedies.

This litany of potential difficulties should not deter you or your child. They are not worse, for example, than the problems diabetics experience. Many people all over the world have been taking lithium for many years without serious complications. However, this, like many other medical treatments, is a delicate matter that needs to be carefully monitored.

FISH OIL, FLAX SEED OIL AND EVENING PRIMROSE OIL IN BIPOLAR DISORDER

There has been increasing interest recently in the role of essential fatty acids in mental illness. They are called 'essential' because the body does not manufacture them and they must be acquired through foods. Essential fatty acids are often referred to as omega-3 and omega-6 fatty acids.

It has been known for some time that humans are prone to deficiencies in essential fatty acids, for example children who are given strict vegetarian diets by their parents. There are reports of an association between low fish consumption and increased rates of depression, and some studies have found a reduced level of omega-3 fatty acids in depressed patients. However, definite evidence of the effectiveness of essential fatty acids in the treatment of mental disorders is lacking. The most encouraging trial is a preliminary study of thirty patients with bipolar disorder. It found that essential fatty acids administered concurrently with mood stabilisers reduced the rate of recurrence of episodes.

Commercial products that contain high levels of omega-3 fatty acids include marine fish oils and flax seed oil, while evening primrose oil contains a higher proportion of omega-6 fatty acids. During processing and storage, these products must be kept in conditions that avoid excess light, heat and air exposure in order to prevent oxidation and subsequent rancidity.

Essential fatty acids are generally regarded as safe unless consumed in very large quantities. They have the added advantage of reducing the risk of coronary artery disease. Side effects include belching, mild nausea, exacerbation of asthma in some patients and a rise in glucose in persons with non-insulin dependent diabetes. People taking anticoagulants or suffering from haemophilia should use essential fatty acids with caution.

Psychotherapeutic treatment

Treatment with medication should always be complemented by psychotherapy. The type and intensity will vary according to the specific adolescent and the stage of the illness, but it should include at least:

- information to the teenager and family about the illness, treatment and prognosis
- assistance to help the adolescent develop a healthy lifestyle
- helping the patient and the family to identify the early signs of a recurrence
- dealing with the emotional consequences of an episode
- helping the teenager come to terms with suffering from a potentially chronic mental illness
- allaying unrealistic fear of new episodes that could inhibit participation in normal activities
- how to resolve problems in relationships with family or friends.

What can I do to help with treatment?

Most of the suggestions given for depression at the end of Chapter 6 also apply in this illness. However, the nature of bipolar disorder does present specific problems.

The first is that some sufferers actually like the 'high' of the manic episode. When they are well they miss the energy, vitality and sense of well-being they experienced while ill. If that happens, it is easy to forget about medication and appointments. You can gently remind your teenager of the consequences of the episode for him and other people and that his 'high' cannot be kept under control at will, without treatment.

The second problem is denial. Once adolescents have recovered from the acute phase they tend to ignore the fact that this is a chronic illness. They invent reasons why nothing is going to happen to them in the future ('not me'). They may attribute the cause of their illness to stress or tiredness, or assure themselves that they are 'not going to let anything like that happen again'. Some teenagers will just deny there was anything wrong with them. They may say the episode was an invention of the psychiatrist or of the family, or that the diagnosis was wrong. Something similar can also happen to parents.

The experience of mania can be very frightening, and shame about suffering from a mental illness can be a reason for not wanting to admit there was a problem.

Denial often results in non-adherence to treatment. You can help by encouraging your teenager to continue seeing the psychiatrist at regular intervals to deal with these issues. Encouraging attendance at meetings of mainstream self-support groups may also be helpful.

Another way in which you can be helpful is in spotting the early signs of a new episode. Keeping a diary of important happenings and changes can help you detect these signs. If there is a pattern, it will become clear after a couple of episodes. For example, some people begin attending church more often or become unusually preoccupied by religious matters, others become promiscuous; for some sleeplessness is the first sign, while for others it is doing a spring cleaning in autumn or going on a shopping spree. Stopping the medication might be the first sign that everything is not well in some sufferers. Often relatives, friends or teachers notice these changes while the adolescent doesn't.

> *Music, videos, activity and noise can stimulate manic adolescents and make them worse.*

Treatment during the early stages may abort an episode. It is also important to stick with one psychiatrist who knows your child well. The consultant will be aware of the early signs as well, will know the treatment best suited to your child and be familiar with side effects. Continuity of care can make an enormous difference in the long term.

You can help your child during a manic phase by creating a calm environment and a routine at home. Music, videos, activity and noise can stimulate manic adolescents and make them more active or agitated. They need a room in which to pace or do some gentle exercise to use some of their energy.

Questions parents frequently ask

Should adolescents tell at work or at school?

This is a complex matter because many people still have prejudices about mental illnesses. You need to think carefully about your child's situation and discuss it with your family and doctor. Because this condition can impair judgment, it may be necessary to inform appropriate supervisors if the teenager's work involves responsibilities which, if not met, can result in considerable harm to other people. This is no different from what may happen with other illnesses such as epilepsy. For example, medical practitioners who suffer from bipolar disorder can continue practising medicine if the treating psychiatrist thinks they are well enough to do so. However, the medical registration board needs to be informed and requires as a condition of practice regular consultations with a psychiatrist.

Should they tell their partners?

Would you tell your partner if you had diabetes or asthma? What is different about this illness? Their partners, if they are in a stable relationship, should know because this condition can have relapses. A frank discussion of the situation and learning what to do if symptoms appear will avoid many problems in the future. Spouses who know and accept their partner's illness can be very helpful, while lack of knowledge will only add to the problems.

What about pregnancy?

Becoming pregnant and having children may present specific risks that will need to be discussed with the psychiatrist and obstetrician. However, most people with this illness can successfully have children. Some medications should not be taken (they can produce deformities in the child) if pregnancy is planned. Childbirth may also trigger a new episode.

It is important that parents are aware of the risks for their children: a moderately increased risk of suffering from the disorder. In some severe cases there may be other concerns. For example, if there are frequent relapses even with treatment or if the recovery between episodes is far from complete, the sufferer might not be able to look after or provide for the children.

Will maintenance treatment influence fitness or interfere with physical exercise?

A well-monitored and stable treatment will not interfere with moderate physical exercise. However, young people ought to be mindful that dehydration can cause toxic symptoms if taking lithium. When exercising, they need to drink plenty of liquids, particularly if there is profuse perspiration. It is advisable to drink water or low-calorie soft drinks to avoid gaining weight.

Suicidal behaviour

Suicidal and self-destructive behaviour is a very worrying development that often appears during adolescence. This chapter will give you an idea of the extent of this problem and its complexity. You will also learn the circumstances that bring suicidal behaviour about, how to assess its severity and what to do about it. Suicidal behaviour usually occurs as a crisis. The people close to the teenager at the time are the ones best placed to intervene and prevent the suicidal act.

Few events evoke more painful and mixed emotions in parents than a child's suicidal death. Guilt ('What did we do wrong?'), anger ('Why did he do this to us?'), blame ('If her mother had been more strict this wouldn't have happened'), sadness ('I'll never be able to laugh again'), loss ('It's as if I've lost an arm or a part of my body') and, above all, puzzlement ('Why? ... he had everything! Why?') are some of the feelings that parents experience.

We, as a community, also find it hard to understand why someone, particularly a young person, would want to self-destroy. Our helplessness in preventing such an action increases our anger and frustration.

Suicidal behaviour is as old as humankind. It has intrigued philosophers, theologians, sociologists, psychiatrists and writers over the ages. Much has been written about it but we don't seem any the wiser.

In recent years the issues surrounding suicidal behaviour have been complicated by the alarm created by media reports. Sensational allegations of a marked increase in suicidal behaviour and suicide deaths, particularly among the young, have resulted in a climate of anxiety.

It would take too much space to do justice to all these issues. The focus of this chapter is more practical: what we know about suicidal behaviour and how we can try to prevent it.

ATTITUDES TOWARDS SUICIDE

Attitudes towards suicide have varied throughout history and between cultures: some condemned it, some praised it. Convicted criminals were permitted to take their own lives in ancient Greece. Japanese noblemen were admired when they ritually disembowelled themselves (harakiri) as self-punishment, to avoid humiliation or to shame their enemies. Buddhist monks burned themselves alive as a form of social or political protest. By contrast, in the fourteenth century, Dante, in his *Divine Comedy*, placed the people who had killed themselves in the last circle of hell. They were depicted as dead trees and were the only ones unable to recover their bodies, which they had voluntarily relinquished.

Most Western countries had laws making suicide a crime. These have gradually been abolished. The approach that focused on punishment has given way to understanding and prevention. Changes in the law do not seem to have had an effect on the rates of suicide.

Suicidal behaviour

Suicidal behaviour comprises a wide range of self-injurious thoughts or actions with different degrees of intent of self-destruction: from no suicidal behaviour at one end to successful suicide (often referred to as completed suicide) at the other. In between there are suicidal thoughts, gestures and suicide attempts of different severity. The last are often called attempted suicide but have received many other names such as parasuicide or deliberate self-injury.

> *Suicidal behaviour comprises a wide range of self-injurious thoughts or actions with different degrees of intent of self-destruction.*

'Suicidal behaviour' is a blanket description that covers many different things, from teenagers telling a parent in an argument 'I wish I were dead', to others found comatose in a car after trying to gas themselves. Some of these behaviours might be related to suicide, some may not. What might be an irrelevant remark to get back at parents in one case may be a clear statement of what another young person is intending to do. Even some actions that result in death might not be suicidal at all but an accident, for example, a teenager who inadvertently overdoses on heroin because the heroin supplied was of much better quality than usual. There is no way to know the seriousness of the suicidal intent by looking at the deed. Whether it is suicidal behaviour or not will largely depend on the meaning of the thought or act for each adolescent: on the intent.

Factors associated with suicidal behaviour in teenagers

Age

There are substantial differences according to age. Completed suicide is more common in elderly people; attempted suicide is particularly frequent during adolescence.

Sex

Boys are about four times more likely to kill themselves than girls, while girls are about twice as likely to attempt suicide and three times more likely to report suicidal thoughts. Most experts believe the higher success rate in males is due to their using more lethal means, such as guns, hanging or gassing, while females favour self-poisoning, such as taking an overdose of medication.

Mental health problems

As recently as twenty years ago it was widely believed that mental health problems were not an important factor in youth suicide. This was contrary to what had been convincingly demonstrated for adults. Studies have conclusively shown this not to be the case. Most adolescents who commit suicide have serious emotional or behavioural problems, particularly depression, before their death. In fact, the presence of a mental disorder seems to be a necessary condition for suicide in young people, although not sufficient in itself. Other circumstances need to interact with mental illness to result in this tragic consequence.

Apart from depression, other associated conditions are disruptive behaviour disorders and delinquency. The last may partially explain why suicide is frequent in incarcerated youth. Young people suffering from schizophrenia also have a much higher risk of committing suicide.

Many teenagers who kill themselves do so while intoxicated with alcohol or other drugs. Drug and alcohol problems increase depressive feelings and intoxication reduces adolescents' ability to control their impulses. Increased impulsivity can also play a part in the likelihood of suicide.

Social circumstances

There is little doubt that social circumstances influence suicidal behaviour. Differences in the frequency of suicide between countries support the relationship. How this actually happens is less clear.

Periods of social stress (e.g. a time of high unemployment), being part of a dispossessed minority group (such as Australian Aborigines or Native American Indians) and social isolation are some of the factors that increase the frequency of suicide.

Suicide and the media

Much has been made over the years of the influence of media depictions of suicidal acts on the frequency of suicide. A classic example is what happened in Germany after the publication of Goethe's popular book *The Sorrows of Young Werther* in 1774. Publication was followed by an epidemic of suicide in young people. This was attributed to the vivid description of the young protagonist romantically killing himself after being rejected by the woman he loved. The book was subsequently banned in most of Europe.

There are studies linking television broadcasts of fictional characters attempting or committing suicide and frequency of suicide attempts and completed suicides among the viewers. Not only did rates increase but the means of suicide were the same (e.g. jumping in front of a train). The most poignant finding was that this seemed to mostly influence boys between 15 and 19 years.

Imitation or modelling, through glamorised media reports or by having friends or relatives who committed suicide, has an influence. 'Copycat' suicides are not uncommon, particularly among adolescents. This places a heavy responsibility on media professionals to exercise their freedom of expression responsibly when portraying suicidal acts.

Firearms

Guns are a very effective method of suicide. Whether their availability increases suicide rates has created strong debate. Easy access to guns has been largely blamed for the high frequency of suicide in country areas of Australia. Similar arguments have been made in the Unites States of America. Reducing the availability of guns or other effective methods of suicide will save lives. However, this has a short-term effect and it would be naive to think it is a solution to this problem. What is more important and practical for you to know is that whether a gun is safely stored or not does not make a difference. Determined teenagers find ways of getting to it.

Family factors

Many social factors have their influence on the adolescent through the family. For example, social tension and stress often result in unemployment. This, in turn, produces financial worries, marital conflict, alcohol abuse and separation, all of which impact on the teenager. Parental isolation, poverty and lack of extended family support increase the chance of conflict between parents and children and make things worse. Harsh discipline and abuse, especially sexual abuse, are associated with suicidal behaviour.

Suicide also runs in families. It is unclear whether this is the result of mental disorders being more frequent among family members, a consequence of imitating behaviours displayed by relatives or an inherited tendency to self-destruct.

Individual factors

Irrespective of all of the above, suicide is an individual decision. As such, it is motivated to a very large extent by a person's view of the world. However, this view is strongly influenced by the illnesses affecting the adolescent, such as depression. Other factors, such as personality and personal crises, are also important. Crises, in turn, may be the result of the adolescent's mental health problems. For instance, someone who is depressed is more likely to be rejected by peers. Peer rejection may then lead to suicidal thoughts. Most suicides are the outcome of a variety of factors that influence each other and create a vicious cycle that culminates in this tragic end.

Suicide is more common in reserved, rigid adolescents. Personality makes it difficult for these teenagers to make and confide in friends and lack of friends diminishes the availability of people from whom they can seek support in crises. Also, being rejected or losing a friend is a more severe blow for them than for outgoing people who have more friends.

A suicidal act is a means of communication. Most people who attempt suicide want to say something, hence the notes left behind. In some cases the suicide attempt is a means to end an intolerable situation or a cry for help. This is quite common in adolescents who have been abused. In others, this may be coupled with strong feelings of anger and retribution. Suicide is seen not only as the solution to their problems but also as the most dramatic way of making others feel guilty for what they had done to the teenager, whether the acts were real or imagined. Suicide threats or attempts are very powerful and can be used to control or manipulate others.

The extent of the problem

Suicide

About 2000 people commit suicide in Australia each year. This is the population of a small town. About 50 000 (this is a guess, there are probably more) attempt suicide. This is the population of a small city. Among adolescents, for every 100 000 people aged between 15 and 19 years, seventeen boys and four girls killed themselves in 1988. Suicide is the second most frequent cause of death in this age group. The first is accidents. Other countries report comparable figures.

> *Suicide is the second most frequent cause of death in young people.*

What is of more concern is that the frequency of completed suicide in boys doubled during the 1980s, while rates for girls remained quite stable. There has been much speculation about the reasons for this but it is still unclear. The number of suicides has fluctuated considerably over the years and this trend might be just part of these oscillations. The increase might also be partially due to coroners' increased willingness to make a finding of 'suicide' instead of 'undetermined death'. Alternatively, it may reflect a real increase in suicide rates.

Suicide is almost non-existent in children before puberty. Frequency increases rapidly during adolescence and continues to climb with increasing age. Suicide in teenagers still represents a small portion of all suicides.

Murder suicide

Murder suicide, although rare, is associated with severe forms of depression. In these cases the person kills the loved ones out of concern, under the mistaken belief that death is a better alternative than living and that dying prevents them from suffering a much worse fate. Women with severe postnatal depression or psychosis need to be monitored closely and treated to reduce the risk of their killing the baby and themselves·

Murder suicide or double suicide (multiple in exceptional situations, such as fringe cults) can be the consequence of a suicide pact between two or more people. In these cases, at least one of them is severely disturbed.

Morbid jealousy can also lead to a tragic end. Typically, a jealous man kills his partner (who actually or in his mind had been unfaithful to him) and may kill himself.

Attempted suicide

Information on the frequency of attempted suicide is unreliable. Several circumstances contribute to this. First, many suicide attempts are never reported. Second, what is understood as a suicide attempt varies according to doctor, hospital and country. Third, many youngsters who attempt suicide are not taken to a health care facility where this can be recorded. The result is that official statistics probably underestimate suicidal attempts by more than 50 per cent. It is probable that, among 15-to-19-year-olds, one in 200 boys and one in 100 girls will attempt suicide each year. About half of those who attempt suicide once make further attempts. Up to one in ten of these will eventually succeed.

> *About half of the teenagers who attempt suicide once make further attempts.*

While suicide peaks after the age of 45 years, attempted suicide has its highest frequency during adolescence.

Suicidal thoughts

Suicidal thoughts increase with age during adolescence and are exceedingly common. Studies suggest that among young people aged between 12 and 16 years, up to 15 per cent of girls and 5 per cent of boys have suicidal thoughts. Parents, however, put the frequency much lower, in the order of 1 per cent. This suggests that parents are often unaware of their child's suicidal thoughts.

The suicidal crisis

For many years suicide was viewed as the result of a logical decision.

> *Suicide in the young is not the result of a logical decision.*

This is not the case. Suicide is more like a crisis, and it is very rare for it to happen capriciously in the absence of other important factors. For this crisis to take place it usually requires a predisposition, a trigger, a facilitator and availability of a method to carry it through. Being aware of this allows possible interventions to decrease the risk at various stages of the crisis.

Predisposition

Teenagers who attempt suicide have a predisposition to do so, in many cases because of a mental health problem, often depression. The distortion in the way depressed adolescents perceive themselves and the world produces thoughts of self-destruction and makes suicide possible. Suicide is not a disease but a consequence, a symptom of this disturbance.

Trigger

Most suicides or suicide attempts take place after something happened that made the adolescent feel unhappy, afraid or angry. Conflicts with other people (parents, friends, school, police) are the most frequent trigger. Examples of these crises are disciplinary crises (when teenagers are found to have done something wrong such as stealing and are awaiting punishment), a public humiliation, the threat of separation from a girlfriend or boyfriend, and disclosure of sexual abuse. These are usually perceived as more catastrophic by the teenager than by other people.

Facilitator

> *Predicting suicide in individual cases is almost impossible.*

The strong emotions produced by crises are more likely to lead to suicide if the young person's judgment is impaired by alcohol or drugs. Other facilitators include identification with someone well known or admired who committed suicide, suicides among family members or friends, or if the teenager lacks firm religious beliefs that forbid suicide.

Opportunity

Finally, adolescents need to have access to the means of committing suicide in an acceptable way for them. Although it may appear strange, people often have a clear idea about the way they would like to kill themselves.

How can I know if a suicide threat is serious?

Suicidal thoughts and threats are common. It would be unmanageable if all teenagers who expressed the wish to die or kill themselves had to be put in hospital or given treatment. Most teenagers who talk about it will not kill themselves. It is necessary to assess the individual adolescent and make a judgment about how profound the intention of suicide is. Don't be surprised, however, if your assessment (or anyone else's for that matter) is wrong. Predicting suicide in individual cases is almost impossible.

> *Suicide threats need to be taken seriously.*

In spite of this, it is an important rule that suicide threats or communications can't be dismissed out of hand. Most adolescents who killed themselves spoke about their intention to someone during the days or hours that preceded the event. Any message of this type (adolescents saying things like 'I want to kill myself', 'I am going to kill myself', 'I know how I am going to kill myself') should be taken seriously until the situation is evaluated by a professional. Once the severity is assessed the appropriate action should be taken.

A RISK SCALE FOR TEENAGERS WHO TALK ABOUT KILLING THEMSELVES

- Is your child a boy?
- Has your child behavioural or emotional problems?
- Does your child drink alcohol or use drugs?
- Has your child suffered a loss, rejection, humiliation or disappointment recently?

- Does your child feel there is no hope or is she depressed?
- Has your child attempted suicide previously?
- Is your child a poor achiever?
- Is your child socially isolated, with no close friends?
- Your child does not have good communication or trust with at least one family member.
- Have other family members killed themselves or attempted suicide?

Give one point for each item that applies to the child and add them up. The higher the score, the higher the risk is. Low scores do not necessarily imply low risk (see the following text).

The scale presented in the box above gives you an idea of how severe the situation might be. High scores will require that you arrange an urgent consultation with a general practitioner or mental health service. However, this scale is no substitute for understanding what is creating the crisis and how serious the teenager's intent is, because the same things may have very different meanings for different adolescents. Often, understanding what is happening is not easy and may take time because teenagers find it difficult, or may refuse, to talk about it. This is particularly the case after a suicide attempt, when they frequently feel embarrassed or ashamed and tend to minimise problems or deny their existence.

If a teenager has been very unhappy for some time, parents may suspect that she is suicidal but be afraid to talk to her about it, for fear of putting the idea in her mind. It is, however, important to talk about it. The risk is not in putting thoughts into the child's mind but in not taking seriously the warning signs she is sending out. By talking about it you may learn whether your child is actually suicidal or whether you are worrying unnecessarily. It will also give the teenager the message that you care, that she is not alone, and provide her with the opportunity to unburden herself, if she wants. However, the topic should be brought up at an appropriate time (not following an argument) and without being judgmental. If your teenager feels that you are going to give her a lecture about the evils of suicide or about how stupid she is to think that way, she won't open up to you or you will end up having an argument. If you think you can't do this, that you can't keep your cool, it is better to ask someone else to raise the matter with the young person. Also, some adolescents find it hard to talk to parents about these issues.

Take advantage of a situation that happens naturally (e.g. both of you are at home and she is helping you dry the dishes), particularly if she mentions being unhappy or having had a problem. Begin with general statements such as 'When I was unhappy I felt that life was not worth living' or 'Once I split up with a boyfriend and I thought of killing myself'. Gradually move on to talk about more specific issues: how serious are her thoughts of ending it all? Has she made plans? What has made her think like that?

Don't let her draw you into discussions about whether this is right or wrong, and don't try to argue her out of these ideas. Rather, give her the message, through words or actions (e.g. a hug) that you care, that you understand, that many people experience similar feelings at one time or another, and that they get over these crises after a while. It is then important to talk about what she can do to feel better or to avoid being overwhelmed by these feelings and what other people can do to help her. Finally, obtain an agreement that she is not going to do anything to harm herself that day.

What can I do to help my suicidal child?

Suicidal behaviour is not an illness but a symptom of something else. In the medium term, you need to address the underlying problems that generated the suicidal behaviour. This will entail a professional assessment of the suicidal risk and what caused it, and it will usually require treating the underlying problems. In the immediate term, however, the priority is to ensure that the teenager is protected from these impulses until she regains self-control. This may mean:

- a short admission to hospital in the more acute or severe cases
- 24-hour supervision at home when less severe or
- setting up supports (e.g. seeing a therapist regularly, having a friend they can contact if need be) to use if the urge becomes worse.

Dealing with the suicide crisis

Most suicide crises escalate rapidly, reach a climax and then subside fairly quickly. Because of this, the people close to the teenager at the time (you, other relatives, friends, teachers) are best placed to notice the warning signs and do something to prevent the attempt or stop it being lethal.

Once you become aware that your child is thinking of suicide, it is essential to clarify the intensity of the suicidal thoughts. To do this, you may follow the suggestions given on page 116. A vague idea that life is not worth living is, of course, much less serious than thoughts about wanting to kill oneself. These thoughts are, in turn, less severe than having actually made a plan to carry it out ('I have been collecting tablets for three weeks'). The more immediate the plan, the more urgent it is to act ('I have enough tablets and I am planning to take them tonight'; 'I am going to shoot myself. I have already stolen the key of the gun cabinet from my father. I will do it this afternoon, when everyone is out.'). These disclosures would be of even greater concern if they occurred in the context of a disciplinary crisis, loss or rejection. Your response to the suicide crisis will need to match its severity.

The priority will be to ensure your child's safety. This requires watching her, obtaining from her a commitment that she is not going to harm herself during the next few hours or next day, and working out realistic strategies of what she would do if the urge to kill herself returns. Even if you believe her answers are honest, it would be risky to leave her alone for lengthy periods of time until the crisis is truly over. Removing the means for killing herself is also a priority (e.g. throwing the tablets down the toilet, asking her to give you the key and removing the guns from the house).

> **An adolescent who is acutely suicidal should be treated as a medical emergency.**

If you think the young person is still suicidal and is not able to give you a commitment that she is not going to attempt anything, you should take her to a hospital. An adolescent who is acutely suicidal should be treated as a medical emergency.

Because of the crisis nature of these problems, it often happens that talking about it to someone will be enough to head it off. The problem is that often no one is available or nobody will listen. Twenty-four-hour telephone crisis services such as Lifeline can play an important role in this regard and probably have saved many lives, although this has been difficult to prove.

Once you have dealt with the issues of the teenager's safety, you can then try to address the problems that made suicidal thoughts possible. Not all adolescents who attempt suicide once are severely disturbed. There are many young people who make one suicide attempt or gesture who don't have serious psychological problems. They will never try anything similar again. Half of the teenagers who attempt suicide do not repeat the attempt. These adolescents will not usually require lengthy treatment.

> *Some apparently harmless over-the-counter medicines are lethal in large amounts.*

Self-poisoning

If your child tells you that she has taken an overdose of medication or has tried to poison herself by drinking something, follow these steps:

- If possible, try to find out what she took and how much. Don't rely on her account alone but confirm it yourself. For example, if she says she drank some liquid from a cupboard, find the bottle, check the name and the amount. If she has taken pills, count how many tablets are missing. Knowing the substance and the amount taken are essential information to give the best antidote.

- Telephone the Poisons Information Centre and follow their instructions or follow the instructions for dealing with ingestion or poisoning on the package. If in doubt, take the child to the nearest hospital emergency service (and take with you the substance ingested).

- Some over-the-counter medications, such as paracetamol, are very good medicines in small doses but lethal in large amounts. Any child who has taken an overdose should have a blood test and, if the levels of the substance are high enough, immediate treatment. In these cases a few hours can mean the difference between health, serious harm and death. Other medications, such as the traditional antidepressants, can also be lethal on overdose.

• After the issues of the child's physical health have been resolved, a preliminary assessment is required to identify the cause. If this can't be done immediately, you need to ensure her safety during the interval. This will mean keeping a discreet watch on her, removing firearms (if any) from the home and locking up medicines. About half the teenagers who attempt suicide try again.

CUTTERS

There is a small group of teenagers who cut themselves. Although this is by no means harmless, and they still have a higher risk of suicide, the cutting itself does not seem to be a suicidal act. Some cut themselves many times over a period of years. Often they also abuse drugs.

These individuals, mostly women, cut themselves delicately and in private. This is typically done with a razor blade, knife or glass on wrists, thighs or legs. They usually say they do it to release anger, tension or because they want to die. They deny experiencing pain. Such behaviour is often the manifestation of personality problems and requires ongoing treatment, usually with psychotherapy.

Chronic suicidal behaviour

Living with an adolescent who is chronically suicidal is hell. If it is difficult enough to cope with a suicide attempt, imagine what it will be like if this is prolonged over a period of time and punctuated by other attempts or by talk of suicide. Sometimes things become so bad that you want to run away, far from everybody and everything. If you feel that way, don't think you are an exception. Any normal person would feel the same as you do. People in these circumstances become tense, emotional and tired. They may end up thinking – or saying or yelling – things such as 'Do a good job next time and finish with it', 'If you continue like this, if you don't kill yourself, I will'.

Fortunately this doesn't happen often. Only a few adolescents will continue having suicidal thoughts or making attempts for lengthy periods. When that occurs, it is a sign of severe problems: chronic depression, a psychotic illness such as schizophrenia, or serious personality problems. Even if you don't see an end in sight, be hopeful: most will not kill themselves.

There are strategies you can follow to ensure a good result as soon as possible:

- Ensure your child has ongoing and adequate treatment for his psychiatric problems.
- Work closely with your child's psychiatrist:
  - Learn about the condition. The more you know about it the better equipped you will be to deal with its consequences.
  - Ask for directions on how to deal with the teenager's behaviour, so that you don't make the situation worse.
  - Find out how to remove circumstances that will upset the teenager or how to create a positive, stable family environment.
  - Draw up a plan of action in case of crisis: who to call, where to take your child, what to do. This plan should cover after hours, weekends and holidays (it is amazing how many crises occur precisely during these times).
- Avoid becoming involved with multiple agencies and professionals. When this happens adolescents often 'fall through the cracks'. There will be conflicting messages from different people, creating confusion and muddling the situation. Unless there are very good reasons for not doing so, stick with one professional and with the appropriate backups. If you have any misgivings, try to sort them out with him or her before deciding to go somewhere else.
- Seek support for yourself as described in Chapter 6. This is even more important if you don't have people with whom you can share this burden.

Realise yourself that you can't keep your child alive if she doesn't want to live. There is a limit to what anyone, including medical science, can do to help some people. Not all suicides can be prevented. If a person is really set on self-destruction, even close supervision in a hospital or prison can't prevent it (but this is extremely rare: the immense majority of teenagers who have someone who cares will have a good outcome).

Conclusion

This topic is particularly sad and upsetting. Every account of suicide is a chronicle of pain, anger, loss and despair, both for the dead and the living. I don't want to leave you unnecessarily worried or upset, thinking that this may happen to any of your children. You need to be informed so that you can detect the signs (if they ever appear) and act to prevent the situation from becoming worse. But remember that adolescent suicide is a rare event and very difficult to predict. We know full well when we have failed but we don't know when we succeed. However, you can be optimistic because in almost all cases it is a success story. Let's try to improve on this.

Fears, phobias and obsessions

D isorders whose main manifestation is anxiety and dread are very frequent among adolescents. They are not easy to recognise because young people know that their fears are groundless, feel ashamed of what they think is a flaw in their character and try to conceal them. This chapter describes the telltale signs of these conditions. They often represent exaggerated versions of emotions that we have all experienced. The best thing about these disorders is that they can be successfully treated.

Fears are much more common during childhood and adolescence than in adult life. Loud bangs and falling frighten infants. Children aged 1–2 years are scared when separated from their parents. Later on children dread the dark, animals, storms, strange imaginary beasts and monsters. After 7 or 8 years, children begin to worry about their performance, while adolescents are concerned about being disliked, rejected or criticised by their peers. The type of fears experienced at each stage of development largely reflects the intellectual and emotional growth of the child at that time.

Fear and anxiety are normal human emotions and all of us experience them regularly. Because children are unable to care for themselves and are more vulnerable than adults, fear has an important protective role during childhood. Fear in the presence of danger makes the child escape to the security of protective figures.

Consequently, it is logical for children to show a greater tendency towards fearfulness, which will decline with increasing age.

The boundaries between normal fear and abnormal anxiety are blurred. The best way to distinguish between them is by considering if these emotions produce impairment, that is, if they interfere with the performance of the tasks expected of a child of that age, or if they cause undue distress because of their persistence or intensity.

Disorders in which the main characteristic is excessive worry or fear are called *anxiety disorders*. These are very common conditions – about one-third of all adolescents with a mental disorder have an anxiety disorder. Although the number and variety of fears decrease as the child grows older, the same does not seem to happen with anxiety disorders. These conditions become increasingly prevalent during adolescence.

Many people think these problems are part and parcel of living and endure them as something that can't be avoided, like being short in stature or not being too bright. This is not so. These conditions are treatable. Although they are unlikely to physically harm your child, if untreated they can make life unnecessarily unpleasant or restricted.

Anxiety, fear and phobias

Anxiety is an emotion characterised by the apprehensive anticipation that something bad is about to happen. This anticipation occurs without a specific, immediate danger. The imagined threat is enormously varied and comprises events such as ridicule, failure, a heart attack, wetting one's pants or even shaking or blushing. Anxiety is usually accompanied by increased vigilance, a sense of uneasiness and muscle tension.

Apprehension about a *real danger* is *fear*. The physical manifestations of fear are the same (tension, vigilance) as those of anxiety.

Phobia is a persistent and irrational fear of objects (e.g. knives), animals (e.g. spiders, dogs), activities (e.g. going into shopping centres, flying, speaking in public) or situations (e.g. parties, crowds) that make the person avoid them or produce an intense desire to do so. The main difference between abnormal anxiety and phobia is the avoidance. For example, adolescents may be worried or fearful about an exam. If, in spite of this, they go and take it, it would be considered normal fear. If they try to do the exam papers but they are so tense and worried that their mind goes blank, this could be regarded as anxiety (in this case, performance anxiety). If they are so afraid that they do not turn up for the exam (avoidance) then it could be judged to be a phobia.

The overanxious adolescent

Some teenagers are anxious almost all the time. Constant worry makes them feel tired, restless, irritable and on edge. They find it difficult to sleep and, when they do, sleep is not restful. They can't concentrate – or their mind goes blank – because of the worrying thoughts, which they are unable to stop. Young people with this problem often worry about their performance (about exams, deadlines, sports). Anxieties can also be about trivial matters such as chores, money or expectations, or about very general concerns, such as the state of the ozone layer.

Frequently, these teenagers seek reassurance, are perfectionists and self-conscious. They are easily startled, 'jumpy', complain of having a lump in the throat, have muscle aches, headaches or need to go to the toilet repeatedly. Sometimes these complaints make parents think they may be physically ill and result in visits to the doctor and tests. Because of the constant worry, concentration on work or at school suffers and these adolescents are unable to participate in activities appropriate for their age.

To be abnormal, however, anxieties need to persist for a time, not just the week or two before important exams, for instance. Always, the intensity of the worry is exaggerated, out of proportion with the impact of the dreaded situation on most people.

These teenagers are called *overanxious* or are said to be suffering from *generalised anxiety*. Between 5 and 10 per cent of adolescents probably suffer from generalised anxiety of sufficient severity to produce impairment. Boys and girls seem to be similarly affected.

Separation anxiety and school refusal

Separation anxiety is the only anxiety disorder characteristic of childhood and adolescence. Because teenagers with this disorder frequently refuse to go to school, it is also called *school refusal* and *school phobia*.

The term *school phobia* is appropriate for teenagers who refuse to go to school because something in the school is frightening them. Often this is fear of being bullied or victimised, but it can be for other reasons. Only some adolescents who refuse to go to school have separation anxiety. A few may be depressed and lack the energy and motivation to attend school, some may be afraid of school for one reason or another (having no friends, feeling picked on by teachers, being embarrassed about exercising in front of peers in physical education classes), others may just dislike school and school work and prefer to be at home. A combination of these reasons probably affects Casey in the case study below.

> *Refusal to go to school is often a manifestation of an anxiety disorder.*

Young people with separation anxiety become very worried when they are away from home or from their parents. They can't stand the separation. Typically this results in their refusing to go to school. However, what bothers most of these children is not school itself – usually they are good, well-liked students – but the fact that attending school means being away from parents and home. What they want to avoid is separation from parents or the house.

Irene, a single mother in her early thirties, came requesting help for her 13-year-old daughter Casey, who had been refusing to go to school. Casey's grades had dropped, and she seemed increasingly unhappy and cranky. When Casey did not go to school, she stayed in bed till late, went out with Irene shopping and watched a lot of television, sometimes until the early hours of the morning. These problems began following a school change shortly after Casey started high school, when they had a change of residence as Irene obtained subsidised accommodation.

Irene mentioned she had felt quite lonely after the move, having lost easy access to her friends. Because she was not working (she was living on a single-parent pension) she felt alone at home and enjoyed Casey's company ('We are like sisters'). Irene had tried to force Casey to go to school but this resulted in bitter arguments, which Casey won. ('I know I am weak. I always gave her what she wanted.') Irene had given up trying because she did not want these arguments to spoil their relationship. 'Casey, like me, never liked school much and is quite a stubborn girl.' However, Irene felt guilty about not managing to get Casey to go to school and was concerned about the effect of this on Casey's life.

Casey disliked school and, to make things worse, did not feel accepted in the new school where she did not have any friends. She was concerned about Irene's loneliness and angry with her for the move. Moreover, she enjoyed the lack of pressure, being able to watch television and going out with Irene when she did not go to school.

This worry is so intense that these children can become physically ill (headaches, vomiting) in the morning when they are due to leave for school. Mondays and the days following school holidays are the worst. On other occasions they need to be taken home from school because they feel sick. Often they are reluctant to sleep over at friends' places, or feel uncomfortable about travelling by themselves or going on errands. When at school, they worry about something happening to the parents (a car accident, rape, burglary, heart attack) and have vivid fantasies about it. Occasionally, they can't cope with parents going out or, if the parents do go, need to know where, the phone number where they can be contacted, and so on. It is not unusual for these teenagers to have difficulties going off to sleep or to need the company of a parent when they go to bed.

Adolescents with this problem become isolated from their friends, lose contact with what is going on at school and fall behind in their school work. They also feel embarrassed and different. Their self-esteem and self-confidence slump and they become depressed. All this makes return to school increasingly difficult.

The onset of this condition is often triggered by worrying incidents, such as an illness or death in the family, a separation or divorce, a change of school or a minor illness that keeps the teenager at home for a few days, but it can emerge out of the blue. Typically, there are times when the child appears not to be worried by separation and periods when it becomes worse.

Separation anxiety disorder is a common condition that afflicts as many as 4 per cent of all children and teenagers. Its frequency peaks during early adolescence and then decreases. Some adults still experience severe discomfort when separated from partner or children. Minor worries about separation are frequent among adults (e.g. if your child is due home at ten at night and does not arrive, it is quite normal to worry about whether something might have happened).

SCHOOL REFUSAL AND TRUANCY

School refusal and truancy are completely different problems. In the case of school refusal, parents know that their child is unwilling to go to school and these children typically stay at home (watching television or doing other things, rarely school work).

In the case of truancy, parents are unaware – at least initially – that their child is not at school. Truants usually leave home as if they are going to school but spend the day doing things they enjoy (e.g. hanging about at the mall or pinball parlour), often in the company of other truants.

Panic disorder

Some adolescents have recurrent and unexpected episodes of panic, that is, severe episodes of anxiety that last a few minutes. During the attack they experience intense fear and a desire to escape produced by a feeling of acute danger or impending doom ('It feels as if I'm about to die'). Others feel as if they are going crazy or as if they may lose control and do something terrible or embarrassing. It is not

Panic attacks are not physically harmful.

uncommon for individuals who have a panic attack to end up in hospital emergency rooms, thinking they might have a heart attack. During the episode of panic they also experience unpleasant bodily sensations such as palpitations, sweating, shakes, chest pain, nausea and dizziness.

Panic attacks are not physically dangerous. However, parents should not make the diagnosis. Going to the emergency room of the nearest hospital may be the appropriate response the first time this happens. Once a diagnosis has been made, such visits should be avoided.

Panic attacks can occur in most anxiety disorders but more often lead to the development of agoraphobia. People with agoraphobia, at least initially, are afraid of having a panic attack. This is why they avoid being alone or in situations from which escape might be difficult, just in case they have an episode.

You should suspect that your child may have panic disorder if he has had several panic attacks, is worried that attacks may come back or is tense or preoccupied about their possible consequences ('I think I'm losing my mind'). Some illegal drugs such as cocaine or marijuana can produce panic attacks ('bad trip') in some adolescents.

Phobias

Specific phobias

Phobias of one type or another are frequent during adolescence. The majority of these are the so-called *specific phobias*. Teenagers with these disorders become very anxious and avoid being exposed to animals (e.g. insects, snakes), situations (e.g. heights, dentists, flying in aeroplanes) or objects (e.g. needles, blood). All adolescents but the very young recognise that such fears are irrational and excessive, but they can't help feeling that way.

Specific phobias are relatively mild. They rarely interfere with the young person's life and may not require treatment. These phobias can persist into adulthood and often become part of the person's idiosyncrasies, something that sufferers, friends and relatives joke about. Who does not know someone who freaks out at the sight of a cockroach? In some instances, however, these phobias restrict the person's life and interfere with the performance of their occupation. Imagine someone who has to give up a well-paid job in a company that has offices in a high-rise building because of a phobia of heights. In such situations it requires treatment.

Agoraphobia

A more serious problem is agoraphobia (the name comes from Greek and literally means fear of open spaces). Adolescents with this disorder have an irrational fear of places from which escape might be difficult (e.g. theatre, train, shopping mall, crowded place) or where help may not be available if something happens (e.g. if alone in the street or the countryside). This 'something' is usually a panic attack.

People with this condition avoid a wide range of situations and often refuse to go out of the house without someone they trust. When severe, agoraphobia causes the sufferer to become housebound. In milder conditions it creates persistent discomfort and tension. For example, if people with agoraphobia manage to go to the movies they will sit at the end of a row and not in the middle, will continuously check where the exits are and will be the first to leave, even before the movie has finished, to avoid the crowd.

I treated a young man who lived and slept rough behind the emergency ward of the hospital and had become quite an institution there. His family visited him regularly and brought him food. He was afraid that if he went too far from the emergency ward (the limit was 100 m or so) something would happen to him, such as a heart attack, and he would die. He only felt relaxed being close to the emergency department. Sometimes, when he felt more anxious, he had to be even closer, in the corridor, to the annoyance of the medical and nursing staff.

A diagnosis of agoraphobia is not made often in adolescents. However, there are some similarities between the symptoms of agoraphobia and those of separation anxiety disorder. It is believed that a number of adolescents who suffer from separation anxiety go on to develop agoraphobia in adult life.

Social phobia

Teenagers with social phobia have an intense dread of, and often avoid, social situations in which they may feel embarrassed. These include activities such as public speaking, reading aloud in class, attending parties, eating or writing in public.

Social phobic adolescents avoid these situations because they worry *other people* may notice they are tense, blush, shake or show other signs of anxiety. This concern, in turn, makes them feel more anxious and results in the very behaviours about which they are self-conscious. Occasionally, this anxiety is so severe that they have a panic attack. Often they worry for days or weeks before a social event they need to attend and try to find reasons or justifications not to go.

Most teenagers know that such fear is irrational and out of proportion. However, they conceal their anxiety from parents and other people by hiding behind comments such as 'I don't like it' or 'I'm not interested' when talking about the activities that make them anxious. Young people, and adults too, can become very skilled at covering up these fears. They know it is silly but their embarrassment prevents them from admitting their apprehension. Because of this concealment, social anxieties are often undetected. They are probably even more common among teenagers than is usually believed.

Social anxieties can restrict the teenager's life and may result in refusal to go to school or in having few or no friends. This, in turn, dents their self-esteem and can be very damaging during this period in which socialisation is so important. Socially anxious teenagers often use alcohol to relax or get courage and are at increased risk of abusing alcohol.

SOCIAL PHOBICS AND LONERS

Social phobia should not be confused with being a 'loner' and is very different from it. Adolescents who are socially anxious like other people's company and want to be accepted and loved by them. Being alone or isolated is the unwanted result of their fear. Loners, on the other hand, are happy with their own company. They don't need other people and even dislike the company of others.

The true extent of social phobia among young people is not well known but estimates suggest that one in five may have this problem. Symptoms typically emerge during adolescence, often precipitated by an embarrassing or humiliating experience. Because of the nature of the condition – talking frankly about it is difficult and covering it up a habit – very few people actually seek treatment.

Obsessive compulsive disorder (OCD)

Obsessive compulsive disorder is a good example of the advances that have taken place in the understanding of these conditions and their treatment. Up to the 1980s OCD was believed to be rare, particularly among the young. On the contrary, recent studies have shown that OCD is relatively common, afflicting about 1 per cent of children and adolescents. Our understanding of the nature of the illness has also changed dramatically. For many years OCD was believed to be the result of unhealthy psychological processes (e.g. impulses of an aggressive or sexual nature that had been repressed into the unconscious) and best treated with insight-oriented psychotherapy, such as psychoanalysis. Research in the last twenty years has shown conclusively that OCD is a brain disorder with learned and inherited components. In some instances OCD may be caused by an auto-immune reaction to streptococcal infections. Medication and cognitive behaviour therapy are effective treatments. OCD is characterised by persistent obsessions with or without compulsions. The case study of Bruce in Chapter 3 is a good example of OCD.

Obsessions are persistent, repetitive thoughts or images that come to the mind in spite of not being wanted. They are unwelcome guests who don't want to leave and it is very difficult to get rid of them. They are like those tunes that get into your mind and you find yourself humming them in the most inappropriate places. The more you try to throw them out the more stubborn they become. Obsessions cause marked anxiety.

Typically, obsessions comprise thoughts of being contaminated (by touching something or someone), worry about aggressive or inappropriate impulses (e.g. the feeling that you might shout an obscenity while in church or stab someone), persistent doubts about having done something properly (e.g. switching off a light, locking a door, turning off taps) or concern about things being tidy or in a specific order.

Compulsions, also called *rituals*, are physical or mental behaviours performed in a specific way to neutralise the worry produced by the obsessive thoughts. For example, shaking hands triggers persistent thoughts of contamination: 'I may catch AIDS'(obsession). This makes the person tense and anxious. Washing the hands thoroughly (compulsion) relieves the fear and makes the thoughts of being contaminated go away, at least for a while. Doubts about whether the door is locked (obsession) may make an adolescent apprehensive. This leads to checking whether it is actually locked (ritual). This checking lessens the anxiety ('Yes, it is locked'). All these behaviours are normal. What is abnormal is the fact that people with this condition can't stop themselves from carrying out the ritual, often three, four or even hundreds of times. If they don't perform the ritual, the anxiety becomes very intense. Some superstitions (e.g. having to touch wood to ward off evil) have a similar quality.

Most people experience these thoughts and impulses but dismiss them easily. Individuals with OCD can't do that. They are invaded by these thoughts and compelled to repeat their rituals again and again. Carrying out the rituals, on the other hand, strengthens the behaviour. In many cases OCD symptoms have permeated most aspects of their life. They may need to wash and get dressed in a determined way, to check that eating utensils have not been touched and to wash them repeatedly, to redo essays and homework several times until they are 'right'. This interferes with their work at school, with social interactions and family life, often resulting in academic underachievement, social isolation and arguments at home. They then frequently become depressed or develop other mental health problems. Jack Nicholson's character in the movie *As Good as it Gets* is a good example of the impairment caused by OCD in an adult.

OCD is different from 'compulsive' gambling or drinking. Adolescents with OCD do not obtain any enjoyment from their behaviour. What they do is aimed only at reducing the fear produced by the obsessive thought. Gambling or drinking, however, are done to seek pleasure and enjoyment, although gambling is strongly reinforced by the occasional win.

OCD begins during childhood or adolescence in about half of all cases and affects as many as 1 per cent of people. Symptoms start gradually, becoming more complex and severe as time passes by. However, they wax and wane. There are periods when symptoms become worse and times when they lessen or even disappear. Obsessions and compulsions also change. While someone may be concerned about germs at one time he may develop obsessive thoughts about orderliness or checking rituals at another.

Families of patients with OCD also suffer. Parents or siblings may resent these adolescents' need for reassurance and their rituals, perhaps occupying the bathroom for long periods or using large amounts of hot water or soap. The social life of the whole family is often disrupted because of the rituals or refusal to attend family or social gatherings. Relatives are often drawn into performing some of the rituals or forced to keep special sets of cutlery, towels or other everyday items. For example, a 13-year-old boy refused to go to sleep every night until his mother recited a series of prayers three times. When she refused, he became distressed, angry and abusive.

Most people realise the obsessive thoughts and rituals are silly or excessive. Children or young adolescents, however, may not be fully aware of that. Lack of insight makes identification of the problem and treatment more difficult in young people. When left untreated – and most adolescents are not identified or don't seek treatment – OCD becomes chronic.

What causes anxiety disorders?

The precise cause of these anxiety disorders is not known and so theories abound. The most likely explanation is that anxiety disorders, like most mental disorders, are the end result of a variety of factors that interact with each other, and that they are often reinforced and maintained by environmental responses.

Most anxiety disorders run in families. However, their inheritance is not strong. It is likely that what is inherited is a tendency to be too sensitive, to worry about things too much. This excessive sensitivity makes adolescents more vulnerable to life experiences. Interactions between this sensitivity and experiences often result in a disorder.

Rachel, a very intelligent teenager, had recently changed school. She seemed to settle down well but after a week was humiliated by another girl in front of a group of students she had tried to befriend. All because she became anxious when reading an essay in the English class. She took the incident to heart and began worrying every time she had to speak in class or in public. Although she did not tell anyone, every time she thought she was likely to be asked to do something in front of other people she found an excuse not to attend school, sometimes feigning illness. Every time Rachel did not confront her fear she was, in fact, reinforcing it because being away from that situation made her feel better, relaxed. Avoiding performing in public was a powerful reward that made confronting these experiences increasingly hard.

There are suggestions that OCD, in particular, may have its origin in some biochemical abnormality in the brain. This abnormality would result in something like a short circuit, which would produce these recurring thoughts and the anxiety that goes with them. Recent research also suggests that some cases of OCD of very sudden onset may be triggered by an immunological reaction to a mild infection. There is no definite proof of this yet. Panic disorder might also have a biochemical cause in some cases.

Animal phobias and fear of heights may be inherited remnants of ancestral fears learned by humans over thousands of years. These fears probably had some survival value because such animals or situations can be dangerous. They still have this role in children. Occasionally, they are triggered by a traumatic experience (e.g. being bitten by a dog).

Treatment

In spite of the frequency of these problems it is surprising how little we know about the effectiveness of the various treatments. Most of the information is based on clinical experience and the results of adult studies. However, this experience is most encouraging and there are now effective treatment packages for most anxiety disorders.

> *There are books available for teenagers that explain the nature and treatment of some anxiety disorders in a language they can understand. See Appendix A.*

Cognitive-behavioural treatments

These were mentioned in Chapter 5. They are effective and often result in a rapid improvement of symptoms after a few hours of therapy if the adolescents are able to follow the treatment through. The two basic techniques used are exposure and relaxation.

HERBAL TREATMENTS FOR ANXIETY

There are many herbs, such as valerian, that are supposed to be sedating, soothing or to relieve stress. However, kava is the only herbal remedy with demonstrated anti-anxiety effect. Kava has long been a ceremonial and social drink in Fiji, Samoa and Tonga, where it has also been used as an analgesic, to induce relaxation and sleep, and to counteract fatigue. Kava is the beverage prepared from the rhizome of the oceanic kava plant *(Piper methysticum)*.

A recent study concluded that kava is an effective treatment for anxiety in adults, although there are no reports concerning its usefulness in young people. Kava extracts seem quite safe. The main side effects are headaches, liver and intestinal problems and a scaly skin rash. The last is often seen in people who use kava extensively.

One common element in the treatment of phobias and OCD is *exposure* to the feared object or situation. Without some kind of exposure, treatment is unlikely to be effective.

The first stage of treatment is explaining the nature of the disorder to the adolescents and their families and obtaining their cooperation. This is a delicate phase but essential for future success.

For example, treatment of separation anxiety will require teenagers to attend school and experience the separation from their parents and realise that nothing will happen at home. Adolescents who wash their hands repeatedly will need to tolerate having their hands dirty and resist the urge to wash them for increasingly long periods. Lack of cooperation by the young person will make treatment very difficult indeed.

Tolerating the fear and worry and realising that nothing terrible happens gradually diminishes the anxiety. Consequently, avoidance or compulsions gradually weaken. It is important, however, that treatment sessions are long enough to allow the anxiety to peak and then decrease to a tolerable level. If the patient is left still very worried by the end of the session, treatment can make the situation worse.

Exposure often requires going to the places where fears are worse (e.g. shopping centres, school) to carry out some sessions. These treatments, as mentioned in Chapter 5, are quite active.

The opposite to tension, worry or fear is *relaxation*. You can't feel worried and relaxed at the same time. Relaxation techniques are a very effective adjunct to exposure experiences in the treatment of phobias and OCD and the main treatment for overanxious disorder. There are a variety of effective techniques to teach adolescents how to relax, but they require work and persistence before the adolescent can relax easily.

Breathing

Correct breathing is particularly important for controlling panic attacks. Many anxious adolescents breathe too quickly and deeply. This is called *hyperventilation* and it results in a reduction of carbon dioxide in the blood. In turn, this produces feelings such as pins and needles in the hands, light-headedness, butterflies in the stomach and other symptoms that make the teenager feel sick and hence more worried and anxious.

Hyperventilation usually occurs during panic attacks and makes them worse. You probably have heard that breathing into a paper bag helps in these situations. However, make sure that it is a *paper* bag as plastic bags, if used incorrectly, can result in asphyxiation. If your child has a panic attack, first reassure him that nothing bad will happen. Second, ask him to breathe slowly and not deeply, with the stomach and not with the chest. Third, if a paper bag is available, have him breathe into it until symptoms subside.

Hypnosis

There is not much evidence that hypnosis is effective in the treatment of phobias or OCD. However, it can be useful for generalised anxiety and in helping young people to relax, particularly if they learn self-hypnosis. Because it has some risks, it is important that hypnosis be performed by well-trained and experienced professionals.

> *There are medications for the treatment of OCD that are effective and safe.*

Medication

The role of medication in the treatment of anxiety disorders in teenagers is limited. The main exception is OCD. There is much evidence showing that the newer antidepressants such as Sertraline (Zoloft®) (see Chapter 6) are effective in reducing obsessions and compulsions and are safe. One of the traditional antidepressants (clomipramine, Anafranil®) is also effective. Often one of these medications is used in conjunction with a behavioural program to obtain better and quicker results. Antidepressant drugs are also effective in reducing spontaneous panic attacks and are increasingly used to treat anxiety disorders. The side effects and precautions are the same as those for depression.

The *benzodiazepines* (e.g. Mogadon®, Rohypnol®, Valium®) are very effective in reducing anxiety in the short term but do not treat the disorder. The main concern is that benzodiazepines (or 'benzos' in street slang) have considerable potential for people to become dependent on them. When they are used, it should always be under medical supervision and for a short period of time (e.g. a few days during a crisis).

Jenny was a lovely, caring, intelligent and determined girl. She had always had difficulties feeling comfortable in the presence of strangers. However, her parents had noticed that she had been coming out of her shell during the last two years of primary school. She was making friends and enjoying social activities and sports. She adjusted well to the change to high school and her marks in the mid-year exams had been excellent. Towards the end of the year, her parents decided to go on a two-week holiday. They had not had a proper vacation since the birth of their first child, sixteen years earlier. Since Jenny's father had just been promoted to a more demanding position and the children were now old enough – Jenny at 13 was the youngest of the three – it seemed the ideal time. Grandparents had already agreed to move to the house for the two weeks and look after the children. Everyone in the family was excited when the news was broken except Jenny. She began asking questions about their travel plans, whether they would fly or travel by car.

The following day, Jenny's mother was phoned by the teacher and asked to go to school to pick Jenny up because she was ill in the sick bay. Not long after arriving home, Jenny seemed better and had recovered her colour and energy. During conversations that afternoon, her mother dismissed Jenny's pleas for them not to take the holiday because of the risk of an accident as nonsense. When the same sequence of events happened on the following two days, her parents became increasingly irritated and frustrated with her. A visit to the family doctor confirmed there was nothing physically wrong with Jenny ('probably she is too attached to you').

Her parents spoke with the school and all agreed that, no matter what Jenny said, she should remain in the school until it finished. When teachers refused to let Jenny go to the sick bay and call her parents, she locked herself in the toilet where she spent the rest of the day. Jenny refused to go to school after this. If her parents took her by force – this was not easy because she made quite a performance – she refused to go into class. Once she ran away from school. Her parents were becoming desperate and increasingly concerned about her safety.

At home Jenny seemed unhappy and cranky. To her parents' surprise, she began answering back. She continued pleading with them not to go on the trip and began talking about not liking school. She repeated, in tears, that teachers picked on her and the other pupils hated her. Jenny's mother had to leave her part-time job just to keep up with all the goings-on.

Jenny's parents began thinking that the holiday was not such a good idea after all and, surely, it was not worth the trouble. However, after discussing the problem with other family members, they decided to proceed as planned with the hope that, once the trip was out of the way, Jenny would stop 'playing up'. During their absence Jenny stayed at home with her grandparents and did not go to school. In spite of threats, promises and punishments, her parents did not succeed in getting her back to school after their return. Finally, Jenny agreed to go to school if she was allowed to change schools. Her parents managed to enrol her in a school nearby. Jenny attended two days and then she again refused to go. At this point they took her to see an adolescent psychiatrist.

Jenny was not very forthcoming with information when assessed by the psychiatrist. Diagnosis – separation anxiety – had to be tentatively made based on the descriptions given by her parents and teachers. The psychiatrist explained to Jenny and her parents the condition and its treatment. Jenny was told that, in order to overcome it, she would need to attend school. It could be arranged that she return to school gradually, beginning with a couple of hours a day. Learning how to relax would also help to make things a little easier for her. However, she stubbornly denied there was anything wrong and declared she did not want to go back to school, any school. After several sessions and a few weeks the problem had not changed. Finally – after much persuasion, cajoling and pleas from her strong and committed parents – Jenny reluctantly agreed to an admission to a residential treatment program.

During the first two days Jenny ran home from the program on three occasions and was immediately returned by her parents, as previously agreed. After this she seemed to give up her fight against her parents and the therapist and became more settled. She made some friends among the other patients and began enjoying attending the school at the unit. Her parents reported that she had been much easier to live with during the weekend, although they had had some trouble returning her to the unit on the Monday morning. There were no further problems.

The next stage was Jenny's return to her former school. This began after four weeks in the program. She initially agreed to attend her school one day a week. This was quickly increased to two and three days. After four more weeks, at her request, Jenny was discharged from the program. She was coping well at school, even enjoying it, and had returned to her former self at home. Her parents ensured she was involved in a range of organised activities outside the house with other teenagers (swimming, a church fellowship) and she seemed to like them. One year later, Jenny's problems had not recurred.

What happens if these disorders are not treated?

Most anxiety disorders become chronic when not treated. Their intensity fluctuates, with periods in which they become less worrisome. Many people with phobias treat themselves without realising it. For example, individuals who are afraid of travelling in aeroplanes may force themselves to fly if this is required by their occupation. Fear of losing the job or ambition may be stronger than the fear of flying. By forcing themselves to fly, they are treating the condition and the fear may disappear completely after a few trips. Some strong-minded adolescents see their fear as a challenge to be overcome and end up being an achiever in the very area they initially feared. For example, someone afraid of heights may take up parachuting and become a champion in this endeavour.

When not treated, anxiety disorders often become chronic.

What happens in the long term depends very much on the personality of the adolescent and the intensity of the condition. Severe forms of panic, agoraphobia or OCD can be very incapacitating, making the young person an invalid unable to do almost anything. Separation anxiety may result in a loss of schooling, lack of education and fewer work opportunities in the future. Social phobia can produce lifelong isolation.

How can I help my child?

As with other problems, it is important to establish if your child actually has a disorder or is just a bit of a worrier. Once you are sure he does have a disorder or if you have a reasonable concern that this might be so, you should seek professional advice. In general, the earlier a problem is identified the easier it is to treat and the better the results. Here are some of the things you can do to help:

- Most anxious adolescents spend a lot of time finding ways of avoiding being exposed to the situations they fear and covering it up. They become very good at it and learn how to manipulate parents to get their way, so much so that it can take a long time before you realise that something is not right.
- If your child has a panic attack, reassure him and implement the measures suggested in the section on breathing.
- If you suspect that something may be amiss, keep a diary of the things he does: the activities he 'hates', what triggers his teary episodes or his temper outbursts, things that he avoids or is unable to do. You will be surprised how quickly a pattern emerges if there is a problem.
- You need to make your child aware that what he does (e.g. washing his hands many times a day) is not normal. There are now books available for young teenagers that explain the nature and treatment of some anxiety disorders in a language they can understand (see Appendix A).
- Have your child learn to relax by attending relaxation classes.
- Be kind and caring but firm and patient with your child, particularly at the beginning of treatment.
- If medication is necessary, follow the precautions mentioned in Chapter 5.

- You will need to cooperate with and support the treatment program. In fact, what goes on at home (like homework exercises) is often as important or even more important than what happens during the treatment sessions. Of course, to do this you need to be informed of your role by the therapist.
- Finally, ensure that your partner and other family members, if any, are supportive and do not undermine the child's efforts.

What can I do to prevent my child developing these problems?

Prevention is always better than cure and, for best results, it needs to start well before your child reaches adolescence. A healthy lifestyle with participation in sports and other appropriately supervised social activities outside the house is very important. Most parents who love and care for their children are reluctant to force them to do things that distress or upset them or that their children don't like doing. Helping them to confront situations that might provoke anxiety will be helpful in the long run. A little pain now might avoid a lot of suffering later on.

Anxiety-provoking situations are an unavoidable part of life. Children need to be gradually exposed to these situations in a supportive atmosphere to learn how to cope with them when they arise. This is similar to what happens with immunity. If normal children were protected from contact with the bacteria and viruses that pervade our environment, either naturally or through vaccination, they would not develop resistance to those germs and would become seriously ill or die as adults when they, almost certainly, become infected by them.

> *Exposure should take place gradually and in a supportive environment.*

The important element is that the exposure takes place gradually and in a supportive atmosphere. If, for example, your child was afraid of water, the solution would not be to throw him into the pool so that he half drowns, while everyone else laughs at his distress and desperate attempts to keep afloat. This would have a good chance of traumatising him for life. You would enrol him in swimming classes with other children of his age, where there is an atmosphere of fun and enjoyment (not shame) and he is introduced to the water and swimming in a gradual and supportive way.

These children are seldom a problem when young. They are usually loving, thoughtful and sensitive. Often, they are also shy and clingy and may have difficulties making friends. Firm encouragement to attend activities appropriate for their age and which they like doing – or, at least, don't dislike too much – will be beneficial. Such children frequently find it difficult to cope with changes of school, particularly if that means losing the one or two close friends they have made. Making friends in a new school will be a struggle. Therefore, changes of school are to be avoided if at all possible in these cases.

The beginning of secondary school is another critical time for them. Finding the school that best matches the child's interests and personality is vital. More important, however, is that children move up to secondary school with some of their good friends, whose support will help them cope successfully with this transition.

The world is a dangerous place but we have to live in it. Parents need to teach their children how to be safe but an excessive emphasis on how perilous the world outside is can be negative. Unwittingly, you may inject fear in their minds, and this can be damaging for some sensitive children. Ensure they know how to be safe, supervise them properly according to their age, but be matter-of-fact and don't exaggerate dangers unnecessarily.

School troubles

C oncerns about schooling take up a substantial amount of parents' time and school is particularly important for teenagers. This chapter describes the more common problems with learning: specific learning disorders, difficulties arising from lower ability, and what can be done about each of them. You will also find information about the role of schools and the all-too-familiar problem of bullying.

Adolescents spend about a quarter of the time they are awake at school. It is not surprising that school plays a very important part in their lives. They acquire at school the basic knowledge demanded for work, and school provides them with opportunities to relate to other people, to learn to cope with rules and authority, and to develop other skills necessary to become well-functioning adults.

Most teenagers enjoy going to school and find the different aspects of schooling a rewarding experience. School friendships are often the most cherished and bonds developed are profound and lasting. However, one in five young people has difficulties coping with some aspect of the school experience. In some cases the problem is keeping up with school work, in others an inability to

> **One in five teenagers has problems with school.**

accept discipline or friction with peers.

It is quite unusual for teenagers to start showing school problems during high school as difficulties usually begin to show during primary school. In some cases problems lessen during high school but more often they get worse. If you are already aware that your child has difficulties in some of these areas it is essential to make the transition to high school as positive an experience as possible. Occasionally, however, parents or teachers may only realise the severity or extent of the child's difficulties during high school.

Teachers are often the first to notice that something is wrong. This is because of the amount of time teenagers spend at school and because problems in work performance or social interactions can manifest themselves more clearly at school. It is important that teachers, no matter what subject they teach, become familiar with the kind of problems teenagers may experience and alert parents.

This also places responsibilities on parents. It is not enough to know that your child is attending school and doing OK. You need to be in regular contact with your child's teachers so that you are up to date with what is happening, academically and otherwise. Far too often I hear parents saying things like: 'Michael was suspended from school. When I went to see the principal I was told that my son had had problems for some time. This was news for me. Why

> **Schools have taken up some of the roles of the family in teaching children social skills, and ethical and social values.**

wasn't I told earlier?' Neither schools nor teachers are perfect. However, blaming them for the troubles will not solve your child's difficulties. You have entrusted the education of your child to a school and you need to work with the school to ensure that it progresses smoothly. This will require very little time if your child has no difficulties but it may take a lot of time if your child is troubled. Such an investment will be worthwhile in the long run.

School and education

A good school, the right school for a particular child, can help troubled students overcome their problems. A bad school, or the wrong school, can bring down the performance and behaviour of a good student. In the last few years schools have taken up some of the roles traditionally held by the family in teaching children basic social skills.

EDUCATION

Education is the transmission of a community's knowledge and values (culture) from one generation to the next. Children are born without knowledge. In primitive societies there was little formal learning and no school or teachers: every adult was a teacher and children learned by observing adults' behaviour. As the amount of knowledge to be passed on from one generation to the next became more than any one person could know, formal education was necessary. Teaching and learning gradually became more abstract as communities grew in complexity. In industrialised societies most children are not exposed to their parents' work at all, as it usually takes place away from home and is often quite technical.

It would be naive to think that children only learn reading, writing and arithmetic at school: sanitised, neutral knowledge. They also learn the values, rules and beliefs of the society in which they live. In some countries this means instruction in an official religion, while in others education is secular (non-religious). In most societies the government controls the type of beliefs or rules transmitted in schools. In Western democracies such indoctrination is not overt but takes place through fostering patriotic or citizenship ideals. In more totalitarian states education is used openly to indoctrinate children in specific political, social or religious beliefs. Conflicts arise when the values supported by a government or transmitted at a specific school are different from those held by a family. This is not uncommon if the child comes from a minority group. Cultural conflict can also occur among people from the same culture but with widely different backgrounds or lifestyles. For example, a child from a poor family may find it very difficult to adjust to a school in which most pupils have wealthy parents.

Choosing the right education for your child

Choosing a high school is an important matter. You need to consider not only the quality of the teaching offered but also the cultural or religious values transmitted at that school. Ignoring the latter may cause quite a lot of heartache later on. Here are some of the questions you need to ask yourself, the principal of the school, and other people you know or who have a child in that school. They will give you a good idea of whether your child may do well at that school or not:

- Am I satisfied with the quality of teaching in the school? Do students from this school have a good track record of success (e.g. admission to good universities)?
- Is the school only interested in bright students or does it also have support and remedial programs for those who have difficulties keeping up?
- Is it a 'tough' school, which despises 'weak' students, or is it caring? Is there a good deal of bullying, practical joking or racism?
- What is the school's discipline and welfare system? Does this school have consistent discipline and rules? For example, are students from this school known for their bad language or behaviour, lack of respect or vandalism?
- Are buildings and facilities clean and well looked after?
- Do teachers and school staff appear happy and committed? Is there a high staff turnover?
- Does the school encourage parents' involvement? Are there opportunities to discuss with teachers concerns about children's progress?
- Is it coeducational or single-sex? In which of these two types of school is my child going to fit more comfortably?
- What are the core values of the school?
- Does it have support staff (teachers for students with learning disabilities, counsellors)?
- Are there supportive programs for students (transition to high school, peer support, study skills programs)?

- Do the interests of my child match the school's areas of expertise or excellence? For example, if your child is interested in football does the school have a good football team? Or if your child plays the violin, does the school value such skill and have a good music department?
- Do I have any concerns about the religious or cultural values of the school? For example, if you are a devout Muslim, would you have a problem if the school were Christian?
- If there are cultural or religious differences, is the school flexible enough to accommodate my more serious concerns (e.g. dress, diet)?
- Is the school close enough to where we live to avoid long travelling time?

Starting high school

The beginning of high school is an important transition for most children. It can be quite stressful because it involves a lot of changes and often coincides with puberty.

Most teenagers cope well with this challenge but some fall through the cracks. Some refuse to go to school, while performance or behaviour deteriorates in others. Most teenagers need attention and support during this transition and it is helpful if you avoid exposing your child to other changes (e.g. moving house or suburb) during this period. It is always easier to cope with one change at a time. You will need to be more vigilant than usual to detect problems or bad habits and help your child deal with them as soon as possible.

Some of the major changes experienced in the transition to high school are explained in the following pages.

Moving from a smaller school to a larger one

While primary schools are small and cater for a small geographical area, high schools are bigger and receive students from several primary schools. Because of the size, pupils can become isolated and the atmosphere is more impersonal. This is particularly hard for shy children or children who are part of a minority group at that school.

Moving to high school together with some friends from primary school helps to diminish the impact of this change.

Changes in teachers and teaching

Children go from having one teacher in primary school to having one teacher for each subject. Sensitive children who need to feel that they have a personal relationship with their teacher find it difficult to cope with this. Also, it is more difficult for teachers to get to know each pupil and adjust their teaching to the needs of each student. Identifying sensitive teenagers and providing them with some kind of support or ongoing contact with a teacher who can become something like a mentor can help.

Having many teachers also means that children need to become used to a variety of teaching and discipline styles: some teachers may be permissive while others may be quite strict. This stretches the child's flexibility and those who have difficulties adjusting to change can become distressed. These children may do better in smaller schools where they can receive more individual attention. Some students only feel comfortable with or respond to one type of teaching or classroom management style. As a consequence they may do well with teachers who exercise that particular style but have problems or perform badly with the others.

School work becomes more difficult and more competitive

Comparisons with the performance of other pupils and grading become the norm. Some children who have uneven abilities or who worry too much about their performance may adjust badly to this change. Altering your expectations and those of your child's teacher and emphasising what they do well rather than what they do less well will make this more bearable for your child.

Responsibility for their own work and the amount of homework increases

Children who are disorganised or who have little inclination towards academic activities may run into trouble when they have to take more responsibility for their work. These children require some structure outside school and they can do well if you are able to provide that structure, as well as helping them develop a homework routine. However, they will need more supervision than other children and this will take a substantial amount of your time. I often hear parents saying, 'He always says that he has no homework' or 'She tells me that she has already done her homework at school'. Usually this is not the case and their mid-year or end-of-year reports say that they don't hand in their homework. You need to be in touch with teachers and know if children actually have homework to do.

Changes in pecking order and culture

By the end of primary school children are the older pupils and younger ones look up to them. When they start high school they are the youngest and at the bottom of the heap (so they feel). They also become exposed to older, more experienced students and to a different school culture.

COMMON SCHOOL TROUBLES

Difficulties with learning:
- Low intelligence
- Specific learning disorders (SLDs)
- Underachievement
- Problems with attention and concentration

Problems with school attendance:
- Truancy
- Refusal to go to school
- School phobia

Difficulties relating to peers:
- Peer rejection
- Bullying
- Aggression

Troubles with teachers:
- Disruptive behaviour in the classroom
- Disobedience and defiance

Trouble with learning

Most children enjoy school. Learning new skills and acquiring knowledge is usually a very rewarding experience. However, because modern societies rely heavily on school performance and achievement, and because most technical learning takes place in schools, children who have problems with theoretical learning have a very difficult time. Because schooling continues for so long – nowadays, children are expected to remain at school longer, at least until they are 15 or 16 years – such dissatisfaction can become chronic and enduring. Not doing well at school is a source of tension and unhappiness. Other students think these children are 'dumb' or 'stupid' and they end up believing it themselves. This results in low self-esteem, low motivation to do school work, rejection of school and, in more serious cases, behaviour problems, rebelliousness and dropping out. Learning problems are to be taken seriously.

This said, you need to know that there is still much argument among experts about what learning problems are, and their effects. Our ability to read, write and use numbers is something that distinguishes us from other animals. These are extremely complex skills that enable us to record thoughts, feelings and knowledge in a symbolic form and to transmit these to others. Ability to read and write has become widespread only in recent years. For many centuries very few possessed these skills, which endowed them with power and wealth. It is understandable that our knowledge of these abilities and of the difficulties found in conquering them is still very limited.

There are many reasons why a teenager may have problems with learning. Some of them may be the result of the young person's personality or make-up and some might be due to the school or the family, as presented in Figure 1 on page 154. Often these causes interact and make things even worse. To help each child it is important to know the factors that cause or contribute to their learning problems.

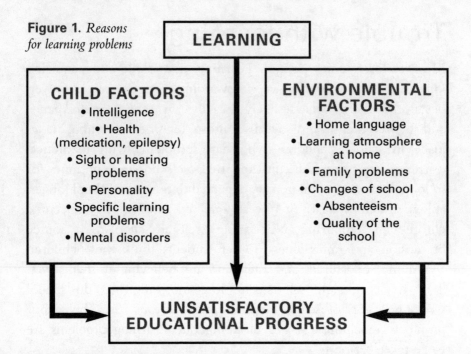

Figure 1. *Reasons for learning problems*

LEARNING

CHILD FACTORS
- Intelligence
- Health (medication, epilepsy)
- Sight or hearing problems
- Personality
- Specific learning problems
- Mental disorders

ENVIRONMENTAL FACTORS
- Home language
- Learning atmosphere at home
- Family problems
- Changes of school
- Absenteeism
- Quality of the school

UNSATISFACTORY EDUCATIONAL PROGRESS

LEARNING PROBLEMS

When a child has an intelligence that is obviously below average (low IQ) and finds it difficult to cope with the normal demands of everyday living, she suffers from an *intellectual disability*. These children's poor performance cannot be considered impaired as it only reflects their overall level of ability.

When children's intelligence is average but performance in tests that measure reading, mathematics or written expression is well below their expected level, according to their intelligence, age and schooling, they have *specific learning disabilities* (or SLDs).

When children's performance at school in most subjects is below what would be expected according to their age and intelligence and is not the result of specific learning disabilities we use the expression *school underachievement*. Low performance in these cases is due to factors such as lack of motivation, poor concentration or depression.

What is intelligence?

During the twentieth century there was a strong belief that there was a general intelligence that influenced performance in most areas. Referring to people as 'intelligent' or 'stupid' uses that global concept of intelligence. This belief was supported by the fact that people who perform well (or poorly) in one type of task are likely to perform well (or poorly) in other tasks as well.

Another view is that general intelligence does not exist at all: what exists is a series of quite independent abilities, such as numerical, verbal, spatial and motor abilities. This theory explains the fact that children who do not perform well in scholastic activities may in fact be very skilled with their hands, the coordination of their movements or in other less academic areas. Most scientists support a combination of both theories.

> *Intelligence is complex. Many children who do not do well in school subjects can be very skilled in other areas.*

Because schools grade children largely on their reading ability or their ability with numbers, we tend to think that these skills are the evidence of 'intelligence'. Certainly, children who perform well in these skills are intelligent, but there are many children who do not perform well in these areas who are very gifted. The problem is that the school curriculum usually caters poorly for children with lower verbal abilities. The result is that they often do not fit well in the school system and this can have long-term implications for their personality development.

Learning problems caused by low intelligence

Most children with moderate or severe intellectual disability are identified before they begin attending school, because of their failure to achieve expected developmental milestones such as speaking, or during primary school. Some, however, manage to go through primary school without this being known. Their difficulties with school work may only become apparent once they reach high school, when the work becomes more difficult. These are well-behaved children who try hard and have intelligence in the upper level of the mildly disabled range or at the lower end of the average range. Often they develop anxiety symptoms, depression or become disruptive during the first year of high school because of their inability to cope with the work.

A psychometric assessment is recommended for teenagers who have difficulty managing their school work. Psychologists and school counsellors are trained to perform this testing and referral by another professional is usually not required. If IQ is about average it shows that problems are not due to lack of ability. Knowing that IQ is well below average will help to set appropriate expectations for these adolescents and the work they can actually do.

Teenagers in the mildly intellectually disabled range may become well-functioning adults who achieve an academic level of about Year 6, can perform low-skilled work and are able to care for themselves. However, they will need more support and supervision than other young people and are more vulnerable to the effects of stress and change, particularly during adolescence. They are also more influenced by the media or older, streetwise peers, and are victimised or used by them more often.

> *About 1–2 per cent of the population suffers from an intellectual disability.*

About 1–2 per cent of the population suffers from an intellectual disability; in the majority of cases it is mild. It can be the result of inheritance or of a multitude of illnesses or traumas during pregnancy, delivery or the early years. Much can be done to improve the functioning of children with an intellectual disability, particularly when it is mild. This is achieved mainly through appropriate and intensive learning and training. It is remarkable that children with similar IQs can function very differently: some may be able to work and look after themselves quite well while others may be very dependent on adults. Early identification of their disability allows appropriate programs to be set up and increases their chances of success.

Specific learning problems

Most people would find it hard to go for a day without reading. Reading is part of most people's lives, work and enjoyment. However, even in countries like Australia where almost everyone attends school, up to 10 per cent of the population has problems with reading. For them, reading and writing is at best a chore, at worst a nightmare.

Problems in the acquisition of reading, writing and arithmetic are called specific learning disabilities or specific learning disorders (SLDs). A child has an SLD when her performance in tests that measure reading, spelling, writing or arithmetic is well below the expected level for her intelligence, age and schooling.

Experts think that about 5 per cent of all schoolchildren have these problems. There are several types of SLD, which may occur in isolation or at the same time. Some adolescents read very slowly and with difficulty. They may fail to read words or may change words and often do not understand the meaning of what they are reading. This is called a reading disorder or, as it was known previously, dyslexia. Other teenagers have serious difficulties with writing. Their handwriting is very poor, they can't spell or they change letters within a word (e.g. b for d, p for q), and their sentences may lack verbs or don't make sense. Often these young people can say what they mean but can't write it down. This is an SLD that affects written expression. In other cases adolescents have great difficulty dealing with numbers. They might be unable to name the different numbers, count or carry out basic arithmetical tasks such as addition, subtraction or multiplication. This is an SLD in arithmetic. These difficulties can cause a lot of problems at school.

Diagnosing SLDs requires a careful assessment, including psychometric and achievement testing. Also considered is whether the teenager's primary language is not English, whether teaching has been adequate and whether the child has attended school regularly.

What causes SLDs?

Early last century people believed that children who had learning difficulties were 'mentally retarded', emotionally disturbed or socially disadvantaged. Because some brain lesions caused by tumours or accidents occasionally produced similar problems in adults, experts began thinking during the 1940s that children might have learning problems as a result of subtle brain damage. This has been shown not to be the case. More recent research suggests that the brain of children with SLD may function slightly differently, but at this stage no definite mechanism has been found.

We know, however, that some reading disorders run in families. That is, SLDs might be genetically transmitted in some instances. It also appears that physical illnesses (such as fragile-X syndrome), problems during pregnancy (e.g. when the mother drinks excessive amounts of alcohol) and toxic substances (e.g. lead poisoning) can cause SLDs.

SLDs and other behavioural and emotional disorders

Young people with SLDs show behavioural problems more often than other teenagers but the reason for this association is not yet known. SLDs appear to be particularly frequent in inattentive, impulsive and hyperactive children, those suffering from attention deficit hyperactivity disorder (ADHD). However, this does not mean that SLDs cause ADHD, or vice versa. The most plausible explanation is that both conditions may be the result of something else. Certainly, treating SLDs does not resolve the problems with attention, and treating ADHD does not settle the learning problems.

What happens to adolescents with specific learning problems when they grow up?

Most of the information available refers to children who had reading difficulties and less is known about the other learning problems. Children with reading problems often continue to have reading problems as adults. However, how far they go in their education and how well they do occupationally largely depends on their social and family background. For example, children whose parents are lawyers or doctors are likely to become professionals as well, while those whose parents are blue-collar workers are likely to end up doing similar work. Nevertheless, teenagers with SLDs usually achieve less than their siblings. Also, these teenagers are more likely to drop out of school, to have lower self-esteem and to become demoralised. However, reading continues to improve well into adulthood if the teenager or adult continues to read and write. The overall prognosis for social and psychological well-being is better than studies carried out during childhood would lead us to believe. Adult antisocial behaviour (see Chapter 11) is not worse in children who were poor readers than in good readers.

Treatment of SLDs

Parents are faced with a bewildering array of treatment options for SLDs. The answer is very simple: the only effective treatment is remedial teaching. Regrettably, the treatment of SLDs has suffered the same problems as the treatment of other mental disorders. Much too often, enthusiastic professionals have allowed themselves to get carried away by anecdotal experiences and to recommend or perform treatments of doubtful efficacy.

Treatment needs to start as early as possible: it can usually begin by the age of 7 or 8 years. To do this, it is important to identify the problem early and to carry out a comprehensive assessment. A concentrated program of remediation early in the child's school career often produces lasting results. Some children with more severe problems may require time-consuming, expensive and ongoing remedial work. During secondary school, parents may be confronted by complications of the learning problems such as demoralisation, dislike of school or low self-esteem, which may require attention and help in their own right.

Is medication useful?

There is no scientific evidence suggesting that medication is effective in the treatment of SLDs. If there are other concurrent problems, however, treatment of those problems with medication may assist in the management of the SLDs. For example, stimulant drugs used for the treatment of ADHD certainly improve the child's ability to concentrate. This may indirectly help learning by making the child more manageable in the classroom and more able to concentrate and carry out school work. However, medication by itself does not seem to improve scholastic achievement in the long term. This is disappointing, because the often dramatic short-term effects of medication raise expectations that it may help scholastic achievement.

Medication is not recommended for the treatment of children with SLDs without ADHD. This is discussed in more detail in the next chapter. If poor school performance is due to other problems that respond to medication, those problems should also be treated. However, no amount of medication will teach your child to read or multiply.

What about therapies that increase motor coordination?

There are theories that SLDs result from of a lack of neuro-psychological organisation or a sensory-motor dysfunction. According to supporters of these theories, sensory stimulation (called patterning) or exercises aimed at improving visuomotor skills will help. These treatments, and there is a wide variety of them, may be beneficial in improving children's self-confidence in these areas but won't improve their academic performance. The same energy and time devoted to more traditional remediation will probably produce better results.

Do diet or vitamins improve SLDs?

Some people have blamed allergic sensitivity, hypoglycaemia, food additives and other food-related factors for SLDs. There is no scientific evidence supporting such assumptions. Many children are subject to unusual and expensive diets, which probably make them feel even more different and have no therapeutic value in most cases. Something similar can be said of vitamins, used in very large doses by practitioners of so-called orthomolecular medicine.

Do tinted lenses help?

There is a theory that some reading problems are due to an excessive sensitivity of the eye to particular light frequencies. It has been alleged that this sensitivity can be treated by the use of tinted lenses that filter out those frequencies. However, this has not been shown to be the case in scientific studies.

What can I do to assist my child with learning problems?

You can do a lot to help your child, probably more than anyone else. But most of what you can do needs to be done early, during primary school.

• Once your child starts school, listen to her reading school material out loud for a short period every day. This simple activity is very effective in reducing reading problems in children. It will also prove to her that you are interested in and involved with her school work, will encourage her to read, and will give you a good deal of enjoyment watching her progress. However, be careful not to be critical or negative. On the contrary, praise her and reward her as much as possible.

• If your child has academic problems at school, organise an assessment of her intelligence and academic achievement during the second year of school. If she has serious problems they will begin to become clear by then. A more comprehensive assessment will be required if learning problems are identified, in order to establish possible causes. Treatment recommendations will follow from this assessment. Treatment may be carried out by school counsellors, educational psychologists, child psychiatrists, developmental paediatricians or specialised clinics. However, be suspicious of the expertise of people who recommend any of the unproven treatments mentioned above. In that case, seek a second opinion.

• Concentrate your and your child's energy in remediation. Discuss the problems with the school and work out with the teacher ways in which the school can provide extra help. Ask for advice from a teacher experienced in dealing with SLDs and seek guidance about what you can do at home to complement the work performed at school.

• Ensure that your child understands the nature of her difficulties (to do this you need to understand them yourself first). Emphasise that she is not dumb or slow but has a specific problem. Some people are colour blind, that is, they can't name or distinguish some colours, but this does not mean they are not intelligent. The case is similar with SLDs. Don't criticise your child's performance or compare it with that of her siblings or other children.

• Help your child to become involved in activities or hobbies at which she is good and where she can achieve success. If this is important for any child, it is even more important for children with SLDs. It is a way of ensuring that self-esteem is protected.

• If you feel guilty because of your child's difficulties, or angry with her or the school because of her lack of success, your expectations may be unrealistic or you may be using her academic success to fulfil your needs rather than hers. If that is the case, you may need to talk to someone about it. Occasionally, such feelings may lead parents in an endless pursuit of a 'cure' and to go from treatment to treatment. This can be tiring or even devastating for your child who may get the message that he has some unusual, severe, untreatable problem.

Bullying

Everyone knows from personal experience, either as a perpetrator, victim or witness, that bullying is a problem in schools all over the world. In Norway, where this problem has been studied in detail, 15 per cent of children aged 7 to 16 years were involved in ongoing bullying, either as perpetrators or victims.

Being bullied is a big problem for many children. It can result in dislike of school, poor school performance and school non-attendance. It may lower self-esteem and, in more serious cases, can cause children to refuse to attend school, to drop out, to become depressed or even commit suicide.

The bullying that I am talking about is not the isolated incident in which a child is called a name or pushed about, but repeated victimisation, overt or covert, over a period of time, either by words (e.g. name calling), aggressive physical contact (e.g., pushing, hitting), gestures (e.g. obscene gestures) or by intentionally excluding someone from group activities.

Bullying is not a mental disorder. However, many of the bullies and many of the victims have behavioural or emotional problems. Depressed, fearful or sensitive children, or those from minority groups in the school, are more likely to be victimised.

Although the extent of bullying diminishes considerably during adolescence, its effects are more destructive at that time because of adolescents' need for acceptance by peers. Overall, teenage boys are more exposed to bullying than girls, but boys are also more likely to be perpetrators than girls.

Bullying often takes place in a group situation: several students bullying a victim. Peer group pressure, diffusion of responsibility and mutual encouragement of aggressive behaviour make such bullying frequent.

What causes bullying?

There are several widely held misconceptions about bullying. The first is that victimisation is induced by external differences, such as being fat or wearing glasses. That does not seem to be the case. Some people think that bullying increases with the size of the classroom or the school. This has also been shown not to be true. Bullying is not a reaction of some children to poor performance or frustration with school work.

What causes bullying then? Two factors appear prominent. One is the school culture: whether teachers ignore, condone or even encourage aggression, or whether their attitude clearly discourages such behaviour. The second is the personality and physical attributes of the bully.

Bullies and victims

The typical bully is usually a boy (but it can be a girl) who is bigger and stronger than his peers, particularly his victims (bullies seldom victimise students who are able to defend themselves). He is aggressive, not only towards other students, but also towards teachers and parents. He has the need to dominate or control others, doesn't understand the effects of his behaviour on other people and lacks remorse. Occasionally, he demands money, goods or services from his victims. He is not particularly liked by other students but has a small group of followers, two or three, who like him. These don't usually initiate bullying, although they often participate as passive bullies or henchmen.

The typical victims are boys or girls who are younger, smaller in size or weaker. They are sensitive, anxious and insecure. They often feel they are a failure and they have no close friends. They are not provocative but react to bullying by crying or withdrawal. These are passive or submissive victims. However, there is a smaller group of victims who are provocative. They are smaller or weaker but irritate and provoke other students and teachers. They are often restless or hyperactive and have concentration problems. They are disliked by their peers.

What can I do to help my child who is being victimised?

Being bullied or victimised should not be part and parcel of growing up. Every child is entitled to feel safe at school. No one should fear going to school because of ongoing humiliation, harassment or degradation. You need to understand this and act, whether your child is a victim or a bully. Victimisation will not 'toughen up' your weak child. If your child is being victimised it is important that you:

- Listen to her without blaming her for this behaviour (avoid saying things such as 'Don't be weak, you need to stand up for yourself'). If your child, who already feels ashamed, guilty and weak enough, feels that you don't understand or support her, she will no longer confide in you and will feel more isolated.
- Find out about the bullying incidents: when and where they occur and who the perpetrators are so that you can come up with practical advice to avoid such situations in the future.
- Think of positive ways of helping your child to gain confidence. Victims are often friendless children: what can you do to help her make friends?
- Is your child depressed? Does she have an anxiety disorder? Does she have ADHD? Depressed, anxious and hyperactive children are more likely to be rejected by their peers. If that is the case, she may require assessment and specific treatment for these conditions.
- Discuss the problem with the school, not in an aggressive, demanding manner but in a cooperative way, to find solutions to the problem.
- If bullying is commonplace in the school, there are school-based programs that can be implemented to reduce the prevalence of bullying and aggression.
- If all else fails, a change of school may be necessary. In this case, find a caring school that actively discourages victimisation.

Dealing with school

The quality of schools, school culture, school principals and teachers varies. However, most school principals and teachers are interested in the welfare of their students. Any dealings you have with the school should take place in an atmosphere of trust and cooperation. A collaborative approach will make things easier, while a self-righteous, aggressive or demanding attitude will make everything unpleasant and difficult. On some occasions schools or teachers may be mistaken or doing the wrong thing, may be making the situation worse by not handling your child properly or may even be causing the problem. Nevertheless, a cooperative, objective and non-confronting attitude will always be the best, at least initially.

- Be involved with the school from the start. Attend parent–teacher meetings, get to know the teachers and the principal. Be open and honest with them, not defensive. Seek clarification when you are concerned about something. Even if you are busy with work you need to make time for these activities. This will probably save trouble later on and will show the school that you are interested and committed to your children's education, not just dumping them there. The more you are involved with the school, the more you will know what is going on and the better the communication between you and the school will be.
- Don't let your own personal experience with the schools you attended colour your relationship with your child's school. Your child is not you and schools are also likely to be different. Your own experience may remind you of problems about which you may need to be particularly vigilant, though.
- Don't focus your interest on academic matters exclusively but look also at emotional and behavioural issues. Many children who do not have problems at home show emotional or behavioural problems at school, suggesting those difficulties may be triggered by peer group, social or learning issues. Conversely, when a child has troubles at home and not at school this suggests that the problems are triggered by something in the home atmosphere. Important life crises (e.g. parental separation or death of a parent) can also influence your child's behaviour at school and the school may need to be informed.

- Be realistic about your expectations of the school. Schools can neither work miracles nor use an inordinate amount of resources to help one individual child at the expense of other students. Unrealistic expectations are often a source of dissatisfaction and frustration.

- If there are incidents that worry you (e.g. bullying, allegations about a teacher's behaviour or performance) do not over-react or prejudge. Try to cool down and be objective. Collect as much specific information as possible about when and where the incidents took place and who was involved. Discuss the incidents with the appropriate person, who may be a teacher, the school counsellor or, in matters relating to a teacher's behaviour, the principal of the school. Try to see things from both your child's and the school's point of view.

- Acknowledge your child's contribution to the problems, if any (she may be the main culprit) as well as the efforts the school is making to deal with them. Children, particularly teenagers, need to learn to take responsibility for the consequences of their behaviour. Shielding them or blaming others will only make the problems worse in the long run.

- Do not undermine school rules and expectations (e.g. about uniform, smoking, violence, hairstyle). You need to support them. It would be quite destructive if you gave your child the impression that such rules were silly or not worth following. This would sabotage the authority of the school. If you disagree with some of the rules, discuss that with the school or lobby for a change but leave your child out of it.

- Don't take it personally, as an attack on you as a parent, if you are told that your child has done something wrong. Ask questions, find out the facts and listen to your child as well as the teacher before making up your mind. Discuss it with your partner and, if you feel very angry, sleep on it before making a decision.

- Try not to just 'react' to events but have a plan. For example, if the same problem repeats itself (e.g. your daughter was found smoking in the school), it is not enough to just punish her when that happens. You need to establish why this is happening often. Is this the result of another student's influence? Is it plain teenage rebelliousness? Has your daughter been smoking for some time and already developed a dependence? Do you or your partner smoke? Develop a plan to deal with the problem in cooperation with the school (e.g. your daughter may benefit more from attending a quit smoking program than from punishment).

- Time seldom fixes anything. If you identify a problem, try to do something about it now. However, do not worry unnecessarily if the teacher tells you it is not a serious concern. If the problem persists, bring it up again or discuss it with someone else.
- Your attitude and behaviour towards the school may influence, positively or negatively, the attitude of the school towards your child. Teachers are only human.

ADHD and conduct problems

11

You will find in this chapter information about the manifestations, causes and treatment of attention deficit hyperactivity disorder (ADHD), oppositional defiant disorder and conduct disorder. These problems are discussed together because they often overlap. Adolescents with these problems show annoying and objectionable behaviour. Their conduct is often more disturbing to other people than to themselves.

Most parents think of adolescence as a time when children ignore rules, challenge the values of their elders and society, and are often out of control. By and large, teenagers are well adjusted and stable (see Chapter 1). However, there are exceptions, the main one being the group of young people who have disruptive behaviour problems. These teenagers are troublesome and a source of worry for parents and teachers.

Disruptive disorders are frequent: they afflict 5–8 per cent of all adolescents. We still know little about their nature and treatment and the gap caused by our

> Some 5–8 per cent of all adolescents have a disruptive disorder.

ignorance is filled with a variety of opinions. Some think these teenagers are the product of a society that is too permissive, too lenient; for them the solution is to be stricter and build more prisons. Others believe these youngsters are further evidence of the breakdown of the family and that they need more love and care. Still others are convinced that these teenagers have something wrong with their brain; treatment would then be medication.

Disruptive behaviour disorders

Teenagers whose conduct is not socially acceptable and who cause disruption or distress to others (e.g. they might be restless, impulsive, disobedient, aggressive, defiant, lie or steal) are said to have *disruptive behaviour disorders*. These disorders include a variety of problems which may be limited to the teenager's home and family or which may affect the school or the wider community. Because of the bother these teenagers cause to the people around them, these problems rarely go undetected and these adolescents are quickly identified as troubled.

John's mother brought him for assessment at the suggestion of the school counsellor. He was inattentive, overactive, noisy and disruptive in the classroom. This had been a serious problem since he began attending high school. In spite of his small size, teachers found him difficult to manage, 'the class clown' and a negative influence on the other students because he refused to follow directions and answered back. He had problems with the other pupils and regularly became involved in fights and quarrels. His mother said these problems were not new and that John was also difficult at home: he argued with his brother and sisters, did not do his jobs around the house, screamed and shouted with little reason and had fits of temper when he could not get what he wanted.

There are three main types of disruptive behaviour disorders. One, already mentioned when describing school problems, is *attention deficit hyperactivity disorder* (ADHD). The other two are *oppositional defiant disorder* (which I will call *oppositional disorder*) and *conduct disorder*.

Adolescents with disruptive behaviour problems share some important characteristics:

- They are mainly male. Aggression, conduct problems, hyperactivity and delinquency are much more frequent in males than females.
- They have difficulty taking responsibility for the consequences of their actions and blame other people.
- These teenagers begin to show disruptive symptoms early in life, usually before the beginning of school or during the first years of primary school.
- Disruptive conduct tends to persist in one form or another for a number of years.
- These adolescents find it difficult to learn from experience. If other children do something wrong you tell them off, send them to their room or give them some other punishment and they learn that they shouldn't do the same thing again. Disruptive adolescents don't seem to learn, even if you tell them what they are doing is wrong or punish them many times.

ADHD

Magazines, newspapers and television broadcasts dedicate a lot of space to ADHD (often called *hyperactivity*). ADHD is a large problem: in some areas as many as 3 per cent of all school-age children are taking medication for it and the percentage keeps going up. Teenagers with ADHD typically have difficulty concentrating, are overactive, restless and impulsive. Those who suffer from severe ADHD are very impaired and can make their parents' and teachers' lives quite difficult. This explains why it has raised so much interest and passion. Yet while many believe ADHD is a serious illness that requires medical treatment, others accuse parents and medical professionals of doping unsuspecting, defenceless children. What we know about ADHD will be discussed in this section.

SYMPTOMS CHARACTERISTIC OF CHILDREN WITH ADHD

Inattention, so that they:
- can't finish anything they start doing
- don't seem to listen
- are completely disorganised
- forget to take their books to school
- seem to have their heads in the clouds most of the time
- anything distracts them

Impulsivity and hyperactivity, so that they:
- squirm and fidget all the time
- can't sit still (get up from the table ten times during dinner)
- are very restless
- are on the go all the time, seem to have an engine inside
- run and climb everywhere
- talk too much
- are the class clowns
- are very loud and noisy
- can't wait for their turn
- seek attention all the time
- do things without thinking
- answer when they are not asked and butt into conversations
- get injured a lot (broken bones, scratches)

ADHD has detractors who accuse parents and medical professionals of doping unsuspecting, defenceless children.

To be diagnosed with ADHD, children must have a range of symptoms (see the box above), the symptoms should have begun before the age of 7 years, and they should cause a substantial impairment in at least two situations (e.g. school and home, school and social activities).

The symptoms of teenagers with ADHD are often different from those of younger children with this condition. Adolescents still fidget and are restless but not as much as when they were younger.

They can sit still for longer periods and are not on the go all the time. Typically, the level of activity diminishes as they become older, particularly after the age of 14 or 15 years. Problems with concentration and impulsivity show less change.

Because this picture, when typical, is easy to detect, some teachers, parents or friends are at risk of thinking that they are instant experts after reading a book or after having seen a few children with this problem. As someone said, 'a little knowledge is a dangerous thing', and there is a risk of oversimplifying this condition. Diagnosing ADHD is not as simple as it may appear and this explains why even experts may disagree about cases.

What causes ADHD?

We don't know for sure what causes ADHD. There are suggestions that ADHD runs in families (has a component that is inherited). Other factors may include mothers' alcohol abuse during pregnancy, lead poisoning and Tourette's disorder (see Chapter 15). Ingestion of artificial colours and flavours may play a part in a very small number of ADHD sufferers.

ADHD does not seem to be the direct consequence of problems within the family or of the way children were brought up. On the contrary, what family dysfunction there is may be due to the impact on parents and siblings of having a child with ADHD. However, family problems, such as parental discord, excessive control or harsh discipline can affect adolescents with ADHD more than other children and cause serious complications (e.g. conduct disorder).

What is ADHD then?

Because we don't yet know for sure what causes ADHD, the best way is to think of it is as a disability, an impairment, something like being short-sighted. There are short-sighted teenagers who are good and others who are bad, some who are thin and others who are fat. The only characteristic they have in common is that they can't see at a distance.

> **The best way to understand ADHD is to think of it as a disability.**

The situation with ADHD is similar. Teenagers with this condition are less able to concentrate on tasks than other students, are restless, more active and impulsive. These traits become a disability, particularly when affected adolescents are in a classroom with twenty or thirty other pupils and they are expected to attend, be quiet and do what they are told. When someone needs to be quick, fearless, not think too much about what might happen and tough, however, having ADHD may be an advantage.

How common is ADHD?

About 3–5 per cent of all school-age children may have ADHD, but the number of cases depends on where we draw the line between ADHD and no-ADHD. Discrepancies in the number of ADHD sufferers in different countries are likely to be due to researchers drawing the line at different points rather than to actual differences in the number of children affected. ADHD is diagnosed much more often in males than females.

WHAT'S IN AN 'H'? ADD

When the H (hyperactivity) is missing from ADHD, the term ADD (*attention deficit disorder* or ADHD predominantly inattentive) is used. However, children with ADD show symptoms of inattention only and there is still much argument among experts about whether ADD is the same as ADHD. For example, when ADD was included, a recent survey found that 19 per cent of all Australian primary school boys had ADHD. This is difficult to believe.

The behaviour of children with ADD is quite different from those with ADHD: they are dreamy, uninterested and unmotivated. These are traits that can occur with a multitude of adolescent problems, from shyness and depression to lack of aptitude for academic work or learning disabilities (see Chapter 10). Furthermore, when some of these ADD children were followed up for a few years, they did not show the same problems that ADHD adolescents have: they were more likely to become depressed, have anxiety disorders or other emotional problems. There are still too few studies of ADD to understand it. What you read here is applicable only to ADHD.

Diagnosing ADHD

Many people don't seem to appreciate the difficulties in ascertaining when a condition such as ADHD is present. They think mental disorders are like physical illnesses such as a fracture that can be clearly seen in an X-ray. However, they can be better compared to something like blood pressure.

Everyone has some blood pressure or they would be dead. But when does high blood pressure become an illness? At 100 mm of mercury? 120 mm? 140 mm? When should someone start taking blood pressure medication? There is no disagreement among practitioners when blood pressure is very high (e.g. 180 mm) but there can be milder cases, and this is in spite of having gadgets that measure blood pressure accurately. Some doctors still overestimate the number of people with high blood pressure because, for example, some persons become nervous when they go to see the doctor and being nervous momentarily increases their blood pressure.

The situation with ADHD − where to draw the line between what is normal behaviour in an active, healthy adolescent and what is abnormal − is similar, but even more complicated, for the following reasons:

• Ability to concentrate varies among children, like their height, IQ or weight. Some are able to concentrate for long periods, others cannot sustain their attention for any length of time.

• Ability to concentrate varies with age. Children of 2 years have a short attention span, while 8-year-olds can concentrate much better on tasks. You can't expect a 5-year-old to concentrate as well as a teenager or an adult.

• There are many factors that can influence a person's ability to concentrate. It is much easier to concentrate on something you enjoy (e.g. a television program, computer games) than on something you dislike (e.g. homework). Tiredness, learning problems, intelligence, depression and a multitude of other factors can modify ability to concentrate.

• Unlike the situation with blood pressure, we do not have good instruments to measure people's ability to concentrate.

• The level of activity is high in children but decreases as they grow older. Just think of the things you used to do when you were young and what you do now.

- Children are able to control their behaviour for periods of time, such as when they go to see the doctor. They may behave beautifully either to impress the doctor or because they are scared.

Because we don't have a good 'meter', the only way to find out whether someone has ADHD is to ask the people who know the adolescent well. Is this teenager's ability to concentrate, level of activity and impulsivity similar to those of others his age? Is it lower or higher? This is typically tested using behaviour rating scales.

> *Parents and teachers often disagree about children's behaviour.*

However, people often disagree about these things. I have experience of men who disagree with their wives about whether their child daydreams, is very active, stubborn or depressed. Parents who are too concerned about children 'not being seen or heard' or are preoccupied with order and routine, or those who are unhappy, depressed or too tired are likely to exaggerate their children's problems. Teachers can also be unreliable: many teachers will tell you that half their class is 'hyperactive'. It is best for clinicians to get reports from parents and teachers so that they can make up their minds after examining information from all sources.

The fact that people disagree does not imply that parents or teachers are lying or distorting what actually happens. It means that different people observe the teenager in different situations and that young people, like everyone else, behave differently in different circumstances. For example, you know very well that some children may be fussy when they eat at home, while they eat everything that is put in front of them when they are outside the family, or they may behave and do what one parent asks them to do but misbehave if the other parent is the one who asks.

Three principles are important when diagnosing ADHD:

- It is bad practice to rely on parents' reports alone. This is not because parents are not trustworthy, but because ADHD behaviours manifest themselves mostly in the classroom. If a teenager shows

> **There is no 'test' to diagnose ADHD.**

ADHD symptoms at home and not at school, that adolescent is unlikely to have ADHD. The opposite, however, happens often because he does not have to exercise the same level of control and attention at home as at school.

- If there is a doubt, clinicians should rely more on reports from teachers, for the reasons given. Also, teachers have a better idea of the behaviour expected of children of a similar age.
- ADHD symptoms should have begun before the age of 7 years. Most cases show symptoms earlier. A child who was not overactive, who could concentrate on school work and was not disruptive in the classroom until the age of 10 years or later is unlikely to have ADHD.

NEUROMETRICS AND MEDICATION

Some people claim that neurometrics (a special type of electroencephalogram, a technique that records the electric currents on the surface of the head) can be used to diagnose hyperactivity. In fact, there is no proof that the technique is helpful.

Others have claimed that response to medication can be used in diagnosis. For example, a mother took her son to a doctor who administered a test to the child. After that the doctor gave him a tablet of a stimulant medication to increase his concentration and administered the test again. The doctor said that the child's performance had improved 30 per cent and that was the proof that he had ADHD.

Although this appears to make sense superficially, the conclusion is not correct for several reasons.

- Most people's ability to concentrate (including yours and mine, not just those who have ADHD) improves after taking stimulant drugs.
- This technique does not take into account the placebo effect (as explained in Chapter 5) and the fact that the child becomes familiar with the test and is likely to do better the second time around.

> • Performance in tests administered in an office or laboratory, in a one-to-one situation (ADHD children usually perform better in one-to-one situations) do not necessarily reflect performance or behaviour in real life.
> • Finally, there are no good tests to measure attention.
>
> This technique, therefore, is not accepted by experts as a way to diagnose ADHD.

How do I know if my child has ADHD?

You should suspect that your child might suffer from ADHD if his teacher tells you that he:

• can't organise his work
• is easily distracted
• makes careless, impulsive errors
• moves about the class, doesn't sit still and disrupts other children's work
• frequently calls out in class.

You would also have noticed at home that he was more active than other children of his age, and that you could not let him out of your sight for a second because he got into mischief. It is infrequent for young people to be first suspected of having ADHD when they are adolescents.

What should I do next?

This depends largely on whether you are worried about the impairment your child has. If you are concerned, or if teachers are worried, you can seek an assessment to establish whether your child actually has ADHD. Child psychiatrists, paediatricians and psychologists can all carry out an assessment. Psychologists, however, can't prescribe medication. The school counsellor or your family doctor will know of respected practitioners.

You should avoid professionals who:

• have extreme opinions about this condition (e.g. those who believe that almost every person that comes through the door has ADHD and those who think that ADHD does not exist)

- use unproven methods to diagnose this disorder
- rely exclusively on your reports and do not seek information from teachers or the school
- are not experienced in the treatment of this problem
- only rely on one type of treatment (e.g. medication) and won't deal with other aspects of the condition.

Treating ADHD

> **Medication is not always required.**

The treatment of ADHD is complex and full of paradoxes. On the one hand, medication is, by far, the quickest and most effective way to improve the symptoms, on the other hand, medication alone does not seem to result in lasting changes and does not appear to influence what happens to these teenagers when they grow up. It is also important to know that medication is not always required.

Because more often than not these teenagers have a variety of problems at the same time, treatment needs to target each of your child's problems specifically. This means that treatment often requires the involvement of several professionals. One of the main benefits of medication is the possibility of magnifying the effects of other treatments, such as behaviour therapy or remediation (if the child also has learning problems).

TREATMENT OF ADHD

Medication
Stimulants:
  - dexamphetamine
  - methylphenidate (Ritalin®, Attenta®)
  - pemoline

Traditional antidepressants:
  - imipramine

Psychological treatments
  - Behaviour therapy
  - Family therapy

Stimulant drugs

Stimulant drugs markedly improve the symptoms of 70–80 per cent of children with ADHD. Their attention in class and willingness to do homework improves, and disruptiveness and restlessness diminish. Relationships with peers, teachers and parents improve because the children become more responsive. Academic productivity often increases.

About 20–30 per cent either do not improve or become worse with these medications. Sometimes a teenager does not benefit from one stimulant drug but may improve with another.

The effect of medication typically appears less than one hour after taking the tablet. It wears off quite rapidly also, three to four hours later. Some teenagers' behaviour becomes worse when the medication wears off. The amount needs to be adjusted carefully over a few months. To obtain maximum benefit, adolescents need to take medication three times a day (one to two tablets before school, one to two tablets at about midday and half that amount at about 4 pm). This may be a problem if they forget to take it or feel embarrassed. However, new slow-release preparations, which will require taking one tablet in the morning only, are being developed. One of these preparations is called Concerta®, which is available in the United States.

> When used properly, stimulant drugs are safe and have few side effects.

When used properly these drugs are safe and have few side effects (see the box on page 180). Dose readjustment or changing the time of day when the medication is taken is often enough to minimise these. symptoms. Overall, side effects diminish after a few weeks of treatment.

Allergic reactions such as rashes are observed in rare circumstances. Pemoline has some liver toxicity (it is seldom used because of this and is not available in many countries, including Australia). Psychotic reactions, although very unusual, can also occur.

Another potential side effect is the appearance of tics (Tourette's disorder). In that case, you should stop the medication and inform the doctor. Stimulant drugs do not cause Tourette's disorder but can bring about the symptoms in predisposed individuals.

There has been concern in the past about these medications slowing down normal growth. Recent studies suggest that this is not a problem. However, drug holidays (e.g. during school holidays) are often recommended. Because most children lose weight it is standard practice to measure their height and weight at regular intervals.

COMMON SIDE EFFECTS OF STIMULANT DRUGS

- Loss of appetite
- Difficulty getting to sleep
- Stomach ache
- Headache
- Tics and nervous movements
- Tearfulness

Addiction does not appear to be a concern with these drugs. Thousands of adolescents all over the world are taking them but there are no reports showing that addiction is a problem. Taking these medications does not increase the chances of abusing other drugs either. The amount of stimulant drugs needed to get a 'high' are much larger than the doses used in treatment.

Other medications

The old antidepressants (see Chapter 6 for more information) can be effective in the treatment of ADHD. Some children improve with them while others don't. Overall, antidepressants are less effective than stimulants, have more side effects and their efficacy often wears off.

Some practitioners also use clonidine (Catapres®) to treat this condition, although there is no definite evidence of its effectiveness. It may be useful in teenagers who have ADHD and tics. There are suggestions that clonidine taken in the evening by children who can't go off to sleep may help with this problem, although combining several medications should be avoided. Because clonidine lowers blood pressure, teenagers on this drug need to have their heart and blood pressure checked regularly.

AMPHETAMINES

K. K. Chen, a Chinese scientist who worked in the United States, returned to China in the 1920s to look for new medications from the ancient Chinese remedies. He found many mentions of a plant called *ma huang (Ephedra sinica)*. Extracts from this plant had been used for more than five thousand years to treat asthma and hay fever. Although a compound from this plant (ephedrine) had been known for about eighty years, Chen discovered its therapeutic effects in respiratory illnesses. Ephedrine is still employed to help breathing (e.g. in cough remedies) and in allergic reactions. The amphetamines were synthesised, after a search for compounds that were similar to ephedrine but more effective.

Amphetamines were found to keep people awake, increase the performance of individuals who were tired or bored, and reduce appetite. They soon became a popular remedy in the treatment of a multitude of ailments, from the morning sickness of pregnant women to depression and obesity. Amphetamines were first used in the treatment of ADHD symptoms in 1937. During World War II, amphetamines were widely used by all sides. Japan, in particular, employed these drugs to make soldiers more alert, to keep them awake and reduce their tiredness in combat situations. After the war, Japan had huge supplies which were placed on the open market. This led to an epidemic of amphetamine abuse (by 1953 there were more than half a million habitual users) and caused very serious social problems. There were also epidemics in Sweden and the United States. These resulted in numerous cases of amphetamine psychosis (amphetamines can produce experiences very similar to schizophrenia).

These days amphetamine (or methylphenidate) abuse is a considerable problem in most countries. Amphetamines are often abused by success-oriented individuals who want to increase their performance. Others, such as truck drivers, abuse these drugs because their work requires sustained concentration over long periods of time. Amphetamines are either purchased in the illegal market (they are easy to manufacture) or falsely obtained by prescription. 'Speed', 'ice', 'ups' and 'crystal' are names given to different types of amphetamines in street jargon. The effects of the amphetamines (taken in much higher amounts than those used in the treatment of ADHD, or through smoking or injecting the drug intravenously) are similar to those of cocaine. People abusing these drugs seek the 'rush' of well-being, a feeling of physical power, of energy and of being intelligent which lasts for four to six hours. This is typically followed by a 'crash' during which the user feels depressed – sometimes suicidal – anxious or lethargic.

How do medications work in ADHD?

The precise mechanisms through which these drugs work are not well known. Suffice to say that they do not cure the illness. If you have a bad cough (symptom) it may be due to pneumonia. If you take the appropriate antibiotics, these actually kill the germs that cause the pneumonia and you stop coughing. The drugs used in ADHD don't work like that. They are symptomatic treatments, more like a cough mixture. If you take the mixture you may stop coughing for a while (symptomatic treatment) but the infection, pneumonia, continues. When the effect of the cough mixture wears off, the cough returns.

Psychological treatments

At present, psychological treatments are considered an integral part of the management of ADHD, whether children take medication or not. These treatments involve education and support for parents and behaviour therapy for the child.

Behaviour therapy aims at helping the child focus on the task at hand, improving motivation and discouraging off-task activities by rewarding on-task ones. ('On-task' is when people do what they are supposed to be doing; 'off-task' is when they stop doing it, e.g. abandon their assignment to tease their siblings, make paper aeroplanes or watch television.) Parents and teachers need to be aware of these children's limitations and set up tasks they can do. Behaviour modification approaches should be carried out both at home and at school.

These adolescents also benefit from techniques that help them improve self-control and reduce impulsiveness, such as 'stop, think, do' (stop what you are doing, think about what you should do now, do it). Because of their difficulties relating to peers, ADHD sufferers often require training in social skills.

The main drawback is that these treatments are time consuming and need to be administered consistently and for long periods of time. They can be very helpful, particularly in preventing complications of ADHD such as oppositionality and conduct problems.

Family therapy aims to inform the family about the condition and its management and supports parents who need to cope with the demands of these adolescents. The first and most important issue for parents to understand is that their teenagers have an impairment that prevents them behaving like other children. They are not bad, although they can do bad things like everyone else. Telling them they are naughty or punishing them for their disability is not helpful.

Families can benefit from the experience of other parents with similar children and there are a number of self-help and support groups.

Some specific problems of ADHD treatment in adolescence

Adolescents often need less medication than when they were younger. The main problem is that they don't like to take the tablets. They think it is not 'cool', are afraid that other teenagers will find out and will tease them, or simply believe that they don't need the medication any longer. If parents (or doctors) put pressure on them, they just take the tablets, don't swallow them and spit them out later.

> *Most teenagers dislike taking medication.*

I was talking recently with a 15-year-old boy who has ADHD and attends a small special school for children with this problem. He is doing well, but he told me that many students in the school who were supposed to take medication, including himself, hardly ever took it. This was in spite of the school having a good system to monitor and administer the medication. Students had to see the secretary at the relevant time. She gave the tablets to the students

ALTERNATIVE AND UNORTHODOX TREATMENTS

There are many alternative and unusual treatments for ADHD, particularly on the Internet. You ought to be cautious before using them. Keep in mind that they may be expensive and time-consuming while their effectiveness is unproven or has been shown to be not effective. Some can even be harmful.

- *Feingold diet and 'back to basics' diets.* In 1975, Feingold suggested that food additives, particularly artificial flavours and colours, could cause ADHD symptoms in children. This theory became well known, received wide media coverage and was embraced by people looking for alternatives to traditional medicine.

  Research findings suggest that some dietary substances, such as artificial flavours and colours, may produce ADHD symptoms in a *very small number* of children. Therefore, 'back to basics' diets may be worth trying in young children with ADHD. These diets eliminate artificial flavours, preservatives, artificial colourings, monosodium glutamate, chocolate and caffeine (and milk products in children with symptoms of lactose intolerance).

  However, dietary treatments have problems:
  - They are expensive and time-consuming to buy and prepare.
  - They should be administered under the supervision of a dietitian to ensure that a balanced diet and good nutrition are achieved.
  - They are reasonably easy to implement with young children, difficult with older children and almost impossible with adolescents.

- *Omega-3 and omega-6 fatty acid supplements* (fish oil, flax seed oil and evening primrose oil). These are described in Chapter 7. There are no studies showing they are effective in ADHD.

- *EEG biofeedback.* This treatment assumes that children can be trained to increase the type of brainwave activity associated with sustained attention and to decrease the brain activity associated with distraction. It is expensive and unproven.
- *Megavitamins and mineral supplements.* Some people believe the use of very high doses of vitamins and mineral supplements helps ADHD. There is no scientific evidence supporting this.

and ensured they had swallowed the medication by looking under their tongue. What she didn't know is that the students had become very skilled at hiding the tablets between their upper lip or cheek and their gums. His mother, who was with him in the office, was stunned to hear this. She and his teachers were convinced that he and the other students were taking their medication regularly, while in fact it was being thrown down the drain. Parents and teachers often under-estimate the creativity of teenagers when they don't want to do something. It is better to be frank with them: if your teenager doesn't want to take the medication, it is usually a waste of time to force him. Arguments about taking or not taking medication also distract you and him from the important matters. The situation becomes even more complicated when teenagers are allowed to carry tablets to school to take at lunchtime: there seems to be quite an active trade in pills in some schools. Hopefully, the new, once-a-day medication may lessen these problems.

What happens when ADHD is not treated?

Not many studies have looked at groups of children with ADHD and examined what happened to them ten or twenty years later, and so our knowledge in this respect is limited.

- Some 60–70 per cent of adolescents with ADHD grow up to become well-functioning adults. These teenagers do better once they leave school and mature. They often find occupations in which their impairment is not a serious problem and it may even be an advantage. By the age of 18 or 20 years many of these young people can't be distinguished from their peers.

- The other 20–30 per cent develop serious antisocial and delinquent problems or an antisocial personality disorder. Antisocial personality will be discussed later in more detail, but suffice to say this is a very bad outcome indeed.
- Teenagers with ADHD are more likely to fail at school. Whether this is due to the ADHD itself or the presence of specific learning problems, frequent in children with ADHD, is not yet resolved.
- Treatment with stimulants does not seem to make much difference to what happens to these adolescents when they grow up. Many people just can't believe this: how can a drug that produces such a dramatic change not have long-term benefits? They might be right, but what research there is does not show a difference.

What can I do to prevent other problems in my teenager with ADHD?

The most important issue in adolescents with ADHD is to let them grow up without developing other problems, particularly conduct disorder. The severity of ADHD symptoms during childhood does not predict how well children will do when they grow up. What seems to be important is whether they were also aggressive or defiant, and how parents dealt with them. Therefore, what you do can actually make a difference.

- Be aware that your child has a disability. Therefore, avoid calling him names, putting him down or repeating that he is 'bad', 'naughty', 'a devil', and so on.
- Try to be positive and affectionate towards him, in spite of his driving you up the wall or making you very angry at times.
- Focus on praising what he does well rather than on criticising what he does poorly.
- Don't try to control him too much. He needs space (apartment living is a torture for these children) and ways of using his energy.
- Channel his energy into constructive activities, particularly sports. Achieving at sports or other endeavours will help him develop self-esteem and self-confidence.
- Ask him to do one small job at a time.
- Don't ask him to do tasks that require a lot of concentration. You will be setting him up for failure.

- Homework is an ongoing battle for these teenagers:
  - Have him do his homework in small amounts. Break it into smaller tasks and reward him with a short break after completing each one.
  - Be with him while he does his homework. These teenagers often do well in a one-to-one situation.
  - Make sure he does the homework in a quiet place, away from distractions.
- Taking medication can also be a problem:
  - Give him explanations about the medication and get him to agree to take it.
  - Don't give him the impression that you use medication to control his behaviour: 'John, you are being very difficult today. Take an extra tablet.'
- Don't give the message that he is not responsible for his behaviour (e.g. that not having taken his medication explains his bad behaviour). If he does something wrong he should be reprimanded appropriately. It would be damaging to let him get away with doing the wrong thing because he has ADHD – or any other disorder, for that matter – although you should make allowances. Make sure that punishments are small, for short periods and immediate. Always explain why and ignore minor mischief.
- Watch his friendships. If you can, ensure he has well-behaved friends who are of similar age.
- Make sure that your partner supports you by spending time with your son. This will give you a break.
- Find a school that understands the needs of these teenagers.
- If he has learning problems, organise the appropriate remediation in collaboration with the school.
- Be realistic in your expectations of what he can do academically.
- Be prepared for the long haul: problems don't usually begin to lessen until these children are 15 or even 20 years of age.

ADHD IN ADULTS

ADHD in adults has raised considerable interest but there are still more questions than answers. Diagnosis is based on the presence of features such as inattention and impulsivity that are persistent and inappropriate and lead to markedly impaired social or occupational functioning. Some of these symptoms should have been present before the age of 7 years. This requires corroborative evidence, such as evidence from parents or siblings, reports of consultations in childhood or school reports. The prevalence of ADHD in adults is unknown but follow-up of ADHD children suggests 1 per cent at 20 years of age and half of that by middle age. Adults with clear ADHD features benefit from methylphenidate or dexamphetamine at a similar dose to adolescents.

Oppositional disorder

Children learn to resist and, if necessary, to oppose the will of others as part of their normal development. This is particularly so during adolescence, when teenagers try to break away from the influence of their parents and develop their own identity. Mild opposition is very common during the teenage years. It shows in adolescents' wanting to do their own thing, in the way they dress and cut their hair. Most parents know this and allow young people some room to manifest their individuality and it usually does not cause major problems. Occasionally, this drive to opposition becomes so intense that it causes problems at home and school. It can result in the teenager prematurely leaving home or in expulsion from school.

Learning to resist and oppose the will of others is a normal part of growing up.

Young people with oppositional disorder have a persistent pattern of negativistic and hostile conduct towards people in authority, typically parents or teachers. These adolescents lose their temper and swear with little provocation, especially if they can't get what they want.

They are stubborn and won't give in. When asked to do something, they just don't do it. A usual response is, 'I will do it later', 'I forgot'. They are touchy, blame others for their mistakes and often seem to get enjoyment from provoking and annoying other people. Oppositional teenagers justify their behaviour by saying that what they are being asked to do is unreasonable or unfair. They hold grudges and can be vindictive.

These problems usually occur at home, where they can result in extreme tension, but they can be seen at school also. Parents and teachers feel frustrated with these teenagers and this often leads to angry confrontations and even suspension from school. However, these angry young people seldom carry out serious antisocial or delinquent acts (such as stealing or running away from home) and in many situations they act normally.

What causes oppositional disorder?

There are many factors that contribute to the development of this problem:

- Some children have, by nature, a difficult temperament. They are stubborn, difficult to soothe and have more numerous and severe temper tantrums than other children during infancy or the preschool years. Occasionally, these traits persist or become worse during adolescence.
- Children with ADHD, learning problems and those who are chronically unhappy often show oppositional behaviour.
- Oppositional disorder can be a stage in the development of the more serious conduct disorder. In that case the teenager's behaviour escalates to breaking rules and truancy, stealing, becoming involved in physical fights, and so on.
- Parents or teachers are often drawn into power battles with these young people. This creates a vicious cycle of increased attempts to control the teenager and ever more rebelliousness on the teenager's part.
- Oppositional behaviour is also believed to be more common in families in which there have been several parental figures (because of separation or divorce) or in which parents were very strict, particularly if discipline was inconsistent and not accompanied by warmth and care.

Treatment of oppositional disorder

The basic treatment of oppositional disorder during adolescence is family therapy. Individual counselling is seldom useful because these teenagers do not believe there is anything wrong with them. They resent being taken to counselling and this creates new problems rather than resolving the old ones.

Medication does not have a place in the treatment of oppositional disorder unless oppositionality is present at the same time as other disorders (e.g. ADHD) or is in fact the manifestation of another condition, such as depression. Depression, which is common, should be suspected in adolescents who have become angry and irritable in the previous few weeks or months. If medication is the correct treatment for the other condition, it may also reduce oppositionality or make the oppositional youngster more amenable to treatment.

Several basic points need to be kept in mind when dealing with oppositional adolescents:

• Learn to offer choices (e.g. 'What do you want to do, John, the washing up, take the garbage out or feed the dog?') rather than one option (e.g. 'John, take the garbage out or else!'). These teenagers need to feel that they have some control over what they do. Involving them in decision-making will meet that need to some extent.

• Some teenagers become oppositional if they feel that parents are too intrusive or unnecessarily controlling. Giving your teenage child some personal space and respecting it can avoid some of these problems.

• It is quite healthy for teenagers to push and test the limits of what they are allowed to do. It is better if you see this as a game that will prepare them for the adult world rather than as their being obstinate or ungrateful. Be firm but don't become too fired up by their stubborn, unreasonable requests.

• Because these problems have often been present for a long time, parents can become unable to differentiate issues on which they need to take a stand from matters that are trivial and not worth the fuss. Parents become afraid that if they give in or ignore something, their child will get out of control and walk all over them. Consequently, parents end up nagging, saying 'no' all the time or trying to set more and more limits and controls. The more you push a spring, the more resistance you get. Parents need to work with a therapist on what is important and what isn't, what is really worth a fight and what isn't (it's futile getting into a battle if you know that you are not going to win).

- When the teenager's oppositional behaviour has been present for years, some parents just give in and think their child is too strong-willed for them. These parents lose confidence in themselves as parents and the adolescent increasingly takes control. This can happen more easily in single-parent families or families in which parents don't support each other in the upbringing of the children. When this pattern is established it is difficult to change. Parents, with help from a counsellor, need to gradually re-establish boundaries between them and the children and take charge of the situation.

- Remember that adolescence is a preparation for adulthood and teenagers need to have an increasing degree of freedom (and responsibility). Dead-end discussions about good versus bad conduct are not useful and lead nowhere. It is better to find out whether what your teenager wants is suitable for a person of his age and circumstances. Rephrasing limits or prohibitions in terms of safety or danger, rather than in terms of good and bad, is more likely to be accepted (e.g. 'It is too dangerous for you to travel on your own at night. I am quite happy for you to go to the movies but I need to be sure that you are safe. I can go to pick you up or you can come home earlier.').

- If a negative, angry pattern of interactions (arguments, prohibitions, screaming) has become almost the only way in which you and your teenager relate, you need to break the cycle. These interactions bring out the worst in each of you and exclude more satisfying interactions. Find areas of common interest (e.g. a father may invite his son to go fishing with him and discovers that his son enjoys that activity). This can provide positive, warm and enjoyable experiences on which change may be built.

- Be creative in your solutions. For example, rather than having endless arguments about how loud his music is you may cooperatively work out a timetable for him to listen to music or maybe you buy earphones.

Lisa, a 16-year-old girl, went for a consultation with her mother, Yvonne (a sole parent), her younger brother and sister. The school counsellor had suggested it because Lisa's performance at school had dropped and she was angry and unhappy. Yvonne said that Lisa had become very argumentative, disobedient and oppositional during the previous eighteen months. She had also shown a silent, sullen anger at home and withdrew to her room when not arguing. It transpired during the interview that the main friction was between Lisa and her mother. When Yvonne arrived home from work, exhausted, she resented seeing her teenage children lazing around and became furious when Lisa, the oldest, had not done the household chores. She berated the children during the evening meal and Lisa was often the target. The situation then escalated and the other children joined Yvonne in her criticism of Lisa, who ended up storming out and locking herself in her room. After these arguments Lisa could not concentrate and do her homework. The following day she was reprimanded at school for not having done her homework, was cranky and came home in a worse mood. Lisa also argued and slammed doors when her mother did not allow her to go out or asked her to come home from an outing at a 'reasonable' time. Arguments often ended when Yvonne grounded Lisa for a week. 'You don't trust me' and 'I don't care' became Lisa's favourite phrases. As soon as she heard them, Yvonne's anger flared and an argument followed. These problems had begun shortly after Yvonne's parents, upon whom she had relied for help and support since her divorce, moved to the country to retire. Because of all these problems Yvonne felt that she could not perform at work as she should and this was an extra worry for her.

The therapist acknowledged Yvonne's and her children's sadness for the loss of Yvonne's parents, who had been a great help and were very much loved by all of them. Their not being around had placed more demands and responsibilities on everyone, particularly on Lisa. Yvonne no longer had their immediate emotional and practical support either. However, the situation could not continue as it was. The therapist gave Yvonne the choice of postponing her arguments with Lisa until after dinner or taking her outside, away from the interference of the younger children, and arguing there. Because Yvonne had been feeling particularly tired and emotional for some months, the therapist, who noticed that she did not look well, also recommended that she see her family doctor for a check-up.

When Lisa was seen on her own, the therapist accepted her desire to be treated as a grown-up. Lisa felt that her mother did not acknowledge how much responsibility she had taken in the household all along. However, he pointed out to her that her strategy for getting more recognition and freedom – by arguing with her mother – was producing the opposite effect. The therapist asked Lisa to think of a way in which she could show her appreciation of her mother. This was to be in the form of a surprise, in such a way that no one would know who had initiated it.

In the following session, two weeks later, Yvonne reported that Lisa had been 'cured'. There had been no further arguments at the dinner table. One afternoon in the preceding week a bunch of roses had mysteriously appeared for Yvonne. Lisa had made no claim to know about them. This had touched Yvonne deeply and led to the restoration of a positive feeling and closeness with her 'problem' daughter. She allowed Lisa to stay out later during the weekend and Lisa felt happier and worked harder at school.

Six months later Yvonne and Lias were still getting along well and feeling emotionally closer. The family doctor had also found that Yvonne had a low-functioning thyroid gland, which partially explained her tiredness and lack of energy. With thyroid replacement therapy her former vigour had returned and this had also contributed to a general improvement in what she could do at home and at work.

Conduct disorder

Society tells children all the time that aggression and violence are the keys to success and glory. They read it in history books where we glorify winners and despise losers. They see it in the streets when they admire the monuments we built to yesterday's warriors. They watch politicians tearing each other apart and successful entrepreneurs aggressively and ruthlessly overcoming their competitors. They receive a daily dose of aggression, crime and violence from the media. Remarkably, in spite of such an environment, most adolescents manage to become peace-loving, rule-respecting tolerant adults. However, some vulnerable young people yield to this tide and make violence, delinquency and exploitation their way of life. They have what we call conduct disorder.

> *Conduct disorder is a major but ignored health problem, likely to cost more than heart disease or schizophrenia.*

Disorders of conduct are an important and difficult area of adolescent disturbance. The toll of such problems on families, schools and society is incalculable, let alone the pain to the individuals themselves and their victims. The cost of this chronic condition, a major but ignored health problem, is likely to dwarf those of illnesses such as heart disease or schizophrenia because of its early onset, duration, severity and high prevalence.

What is conduct disorder?

Conduct disorder describes a pattern of behaviour characterised by breaking rules, deceit and lack of respect for the rights of others. Stealing, lying and early use of alcohol and drugs are some of the symptoms shown by these young people (see the box on the next page). These adolescents also have conflict with parents, teachers, peers and society as a whole.

Typically, some of the symptoms start during childhood, although the disorder usually becomes fully established around puberty.

During adolescence, conduct disorder is often associated with school violence, failure and drop-out, delinquency, drug and alcohol use, damage to property and physical injury to others.

THE SYMPTOMS OF CONDUCT DISORDER INCLUDE:

- bullying, victimisation and intimidation of others
- cruelty to other people or to animals
- starting physical fights
- using weapons in fights (e.g. knife, bat)
- stealing, shoplifting or breaking and entering
- setting fires to cause damage
- vandalism or destroying the property of others
- lying or cheating (to con others)
- running away from home overnight
- staying out at night without parents' permission
- repeated truancy
- forcing others to perform sexual acts against their will.

As many as 6 per cent of adolescent boys and 2 per cent of adolescent girls may have this condition. Frequency, however, varies from suburb to suburb and town to town. It is less common in the country than in cities. It is a worry that these problems have become more frequent in recent years, particularly among girls.

It is worrying that conduct disorders have become more frequent in recent years, particularly among girls.

What causes conduct disorder?

Conduct disorder is the end product of a multitude of problems that have their origin in the child, the family and society itself. These factors are closely intertwined and influence each other. Some are presented in Figure 2 on page 196.

Figure 2. *Some factors associated with the development of conduct disorder*

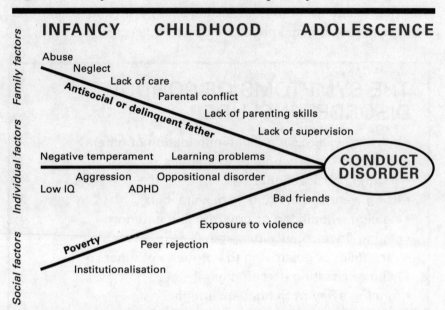

The influence of the family has received much attention. This is because most scholars believe that parents and the way in which they bring up their children is the most important ingredient in the development of conduct problems. One finding that has intrigued researchers is the frequent presence of antisocial behaviour across generations in the same family.

In contrast to what happens with ADHD, there is little doubt that bad parenting – no matter the reason for it – causes conduct problems during adolescence. By bad parenting I mean lack of monitoring and supervision of the child, physical abuse, excessive criticism, parents contradicting or undermining each other's discipline or changing the rules according to the mood they have at the time, and lack of love and affection. Many of these parents are unable to implement and carry through discipline measures consistently. For example, when the teenager does something wrong, the parent typically shouts and berates the adolescent who screams back until either of them, usually the parent, gives up and stops. This leaves the parent and the child angry, with a sense of helplessness and the feeling that nothing has been resolved.

In many of these families there is a parent (typically the father) who has an antisocial personality and abuses alcohol or drugs or both. Having a parent with such a personality results not only in a child who may have inherited a predisposition for antisocial behaviour but who also has been exposed to the poor parenting and family dysfunction caused by the father's problems.

The influence of bad friends is extremely important for these teenagers. You will need to watch carefully what kind of friends your teenage children have and steer them away from those who get into trouble. This will not surprise you, since it is an age-old concern of parents.

What happens to these children when they grow up?

The majority of these teenagers settle down during their twenties and lead a reasonably well-adjusted life. However, up to one in three develop antisocial personality (see box on page 198) during adulthood. Drug and alcohol problems, schizophrenia and other mental disorders are also frequent.

These are some of the characteristics associated with a good adult outcome (the more of these, the better):

- having above-average intelligence
- having no learning problems
- having a caring, affectionate relationship with at least one adult
- having friends who don't get into trouble
- experiencing achievement in some activities (e.g. sports)
- having symptoms appear during adolescence
- having no other mental disorders
- being anxious or fearful
- remaining at school.

Overall, the earlier the onset of antisocial conduct the more likely problems will persist in adulthood. When conduct problems start after the age of 15 years the prognosis is typically good.

CONDUCT DISORDER AND JUVENILE DELINQUENCY

Although these two notions are related, they are not the same. *Conduct disorder* is a psychiatric concept that describes adolescents who show the symptoms described earlier. *Juvenile delinquency*, on the other hand, is a legal term that applies to youth who have broken the law and were caught. Not all juvenile delinquents have a conduct disorder, and not all conduct-disordered young people break the law (most do but are not necessarily caught).

The great majority of young people have committed delinquent acts at one time or another, usually minor ones such as breaking the glass in a street lamp, travelling without paying the fare, stealing a small item from a shop. However, there is a small minority of teenagers who commit repeated and serious offences, such as breaking and entering, and car stealing. Most of these repeat offenders have conduct disorder. They are responsible for most of the juvenile delinquency that takes place in the community.

Delinquency, by and large, is a young man's problem: most delinquents are teenagers or young adults. Delinquency is rare in persons older than 40 years.

Treatment of conduct disorders

Many treatments produce short–term amelioration of symptoms but none of the therapies available is particularly effective in the longer term. Improvements usually wear off quickly. Once these bad habits are established they become very resistant to change.

Individual counselling is difficult and ineffective in most cases. These teenagers are not used to receiving sympathy from adults and they react by refusing it, by being angry with the counsellor or by trying to take advantage of the therapy. They lack remorse and typically believe they have done nothing wrong. When they attend therapy it is often to avoid a more unpleasant consequence (e.g. detention).

A close working partnership between the family and an experienced therapist offers the best chance of success. This should continue for lengthy periods of time: short-term gains are frequent but recurrences of conduct problems are just as frequent.

Residential treatment may help occasionally. Conduct-disordered adolescents require very structured programs specifically tailored for them. Facilities that have a small number of teenagers and that offer treatment for a substantial period are likely to produce the best results.

Medication does not have much to offer in the treatment of this condition. However, because conduct disorder seldom happens in isolation, medication can be useful in the treatment of conditions, such as depression, that occur at the same time.

Darryl was 12 years of age when he entered high school. He had a history of difficult conduct since Year 4, both at school and at home. Teachers had found him very resistant to directions in the classroom. He verbally abused teachers, assaulted other children and destroyed his own classwork or classroom furniture. He often refused to comply with basic rules. At home the picture was similar: he did not want to do chores, deliberately destroyed others' possessions and verbally abused parents and siblings when frustrated. During the first year of high school this pattern was compounded by repeated truancy, stealing from home and the neighbourhood, vandalism and, occasionally, fighting with peers (once he used a penknife).

Two factors seemed to have contributed to the development of Darryl's conduct disorder. First, he had difficulties with learning in English and maths, which made his attitude to school negative and his attention to tasks in the classroom poor. The larger classes, more difficult school work and stricter discipline of high school had made his difficulties worse. Second, Darryl had been physically abused by his father. This only stopped after his parents separated, when he was 6 years old. Darryl's trust in his subsequent stepfather was poor and deteriorated further during early adolescence, as he tried to prove his masculinity with aggressive and defiant acts.

Initially, treatment aimed at changing Darryl's behaviour at home and helping teachers to manage him better in the classroom. However, this was insufficient to prevent Darryl being suspended repeatedly from school. Likewise, although at home his behaviour had improved, the level of support for Darryl from his mother, stepfather and siblings was fragile: they were too angry with him and tired of going to school and other places to sort out his bad deeds. Because of the lack of progress, Darryl was referred to a charity-run residential program that specialised in teenagers with both educational deficits and conduct problems. After twelve months, Darryl was successfully reintegrated into his home and a mainstream school.

What can I do to prevent conduct disorders?

The best way of dealing with conduct disorder is to prevent its development and that is where parents have an all-important role to play.

- Leave a relationship if there is persistent domestic violence or abuse. A broken home is not perfect but not necessarily bad for children. What is very damaging is the experience of ongoing, unrelenting parental violence or discord.
- If you have a difficult baby, seek help and support as soon as possible. You can learn how to manage the child and improve your parenting skills; you don't need to discover these things by yourself. Your family doctor will know about local resources.
- If you can't manage with your children and you don't have other family support, seek help from social services as soon as possible. Don't be afraid that they may take your children away from you. The times when that happened are well and truly over. Social services will work with you and may be able to support you in a variety of ways, such as by organising home help or respite care from time to time. If you don't seek assistance early, the situation may get out of hand and the consequences will be worse later on.
- Seeking help does not mean that you are a bad or incompetent parent, it means that you are wise. Bringing up children is very difficult, particularly for sole parents or when children have problems.

- Give your children a stable environment: move as little as possible, particularly if they are attending school. If you need to move, do so within the same suburb.
- Small country towns often provide a better atmosphere for children to grow up in than crowded suburbs of large cities, even if there are fewer resources.
- Make time to play with your children when they are young and be involved in their activities when they are older.
- Have only one television set at home, even if this creates friction at times. Allow children limited time to watch it and be aware of and approve the programs they watch. Don't use television as an indiscriminate babysitter.
- Involve your children in activities where they are supervised and where they can achieve and meet other well-behaved children. Don't just rely on school for this.
- Don't use physical punishment: it achieves little and there are better ways of dealing with misbehaviour. Hitting children is not only an offence but it is not a productive disciplinary measure.
- Make sure you know where your children are (this applies only partially to older teenagers).
- Know your children's friends and their families.
- Find a school that is supportive of your children (see Chapter 10).
- Don't protect your children from the consequences of their actions (e.g. by writing a note to school justifying non-attendance when they are under threat of suspension for truancy, or by not notifying the police if you find out they have been shoplifting). However, help them through those consequences. If they think they can get away with what they have done, they are more likely to do it again.
- Ensure they don't enjoy the fruits of their stealing. Any stolen items should be confiscated and returned to the owner, the police or a charity.
- Don't be naive and accept simple explanations for things you suspect are not right ('I found it', 'I swapped it', 'Roy gave it to me to look after for a few days'). Check with the other teenager or his parent to make sure what you are told is true.
- Don't give your children the message, by words or actions, that school, authorities or the world are bad or against them (even if it

ANTISOCIAL PERSONALITY DISORDER

Antisocial personality is one of the most serious mental health problems. People with this condition, who are also called psychopaths, are irresponsible and aggressive, do not respect social norms and are unable to feel for or understand other peoples' feelings.

These individuals become involved in physical fights, are aggressive and may assault their spouse or children. They are seldom faithful to a partner. They often exploit their spouses and drift from one unsatisfactory relationship to another. They use people for their own ends, lie, cheat, don't feel sympathy for their victims or remorse for doing wrong. They even justify their hurting or mistreating others by blaming their victims. Although such a description is horrifying, people with this problem can be superficially charming and skilled at conning others. A few may even succeed in public life or business.

These people abuse alcohol or drugs, have arrests because of fighting, drink-driving, rape or other delinquent acts. They are often unemployed or dependent on welfare. They suffer more often from schizophrenia, bipolar disorder and other mental disorders. They are unhappy, lonely people who often die young as a consequence of accidents, being murdered or committing suicide. They usually leave behind a trail of victims, broken homes, abused partners and neglected children. These children are at a very high risk of developing conduct disorder and an antisocial personality themselves, thus perpetuating the problem. Those who survive to celebrate their fortieth birthday mellow somewhat.

is true in some cases). This attitude will only fuel their blaming others for their problems.

• If you lie, cheat or break the law, you can't expect your children to do differently.

There are few services to treat these problems. Clinical experience indicates that, once they are present, the question of treatment is often secondary to the task of helping an overstressed and under-resourced family provide more adequate care and control. Thus, the interface between health services, the legal system and welfare is very important. Regrettably, such cooperation is the exception rather than the rule. The reaction of politicians, the media and the general public is often to put more police on the street, build more prisons or similar repressive measures. These have been shown to be ineffective again and again. The only hope lies in supporting and helping families as early and as much as possible.

Eating and dieting

12

I t is an enigma to see people starving themselves, even to death, in countries where food is plentiful. Those individuals are often teenagers with eating disorders. These are serious illnesses that afflict an increasing number of young women. However, there are effective treatments, particularly when applied early. This chapter was written largely by Dr Jean Starling. She is a child and adolescent psychiatrist with long experience treating teenagers with eating disorders.

Today's children, teenagers and families are continuously bombarded with mixed messages about food. On the one hand there has never been such a concerted effort to teach us how bad for our health it is to be overweight or indulge in eating fatty foods; on the other, the media unrelentingly tell us that ready-prepared, fatty foods are appetising, sexy, cheap – and don't require cooking or washing up. While obesity experts see dieting as a solution for many problems, specialists on eating disorders view dieting as central to their patients' predicament. Society is obsessed with fit, lean bodies and, at the same time, with pre-prepared, high-fat and high sugar foods. Teenagers and parents find themselves in the centre of this tug-of-war.

The pursuit of the perfect body

There have been many advances for young women, including increased access to education and widening career options, but other changes have been less positive. Role models for teenage girls include fashion stars whose careers are based on maintaining a very low, unhealthy weight. The ideal body shape for women has also changed. A curvaceous body, even fat by today's standards, was considered the ideal prior to the twentieth century. Over the last thirty years, a very slim and, at times, waif-like body has become the ideal. It is little wonder that most teenagers find such body shape unattainable. Nevertheless, they can convince themselves that everything in their life would be okay if only they could lose weight, that improving their looks will help them be more popular and more successful.

These concerns are not restricted to young women; teenage boys are also increasingly under pressure to have a perfect body. The media are using more images of men's bodies to sell products. Young male actors and singers are expected to look good. As an extension of this, dieting and exercise are an increasingly popular topic of conversation among young men.

THE WEIGHT CONTROL BATTLE

Most young women have tried to lose weight by dieting, and 95 per cent of Australian teenagers have dieted at least once. At any time a quarter of all high-school girls admit to being on a diet. The average age at which North American girls begin their first diet is 10 years. Vomiting – to get rid of what is felt to be an excessive amount of food eaten – has been used by at least one in ten young women. One in three will fast to lose weight, and the same number say that they have eating binges.

Dieting in normal teenagers

Young women use many methods to lose weight. Not eating between meals, avoiding high-fat foods and exercising are sensible and healthy. However, these techniques do not provide quick results and are hard to maintain. Because most teenagers are impatient and like rapid solutions, they become tired of this quickly.

Skipping meals is a faster and relatively painless way of reducing the amount of food they eat. They deny being hungry at breakfast or say that they have no time. They may then move on to skipping lunch, often by throwing away a packed lunch or lying about buying something. Luckily, the majority do this for a short period and then become so hungry that they give up.

PICKY AND FUSSY EATERS

Teenagers, mainly younger ones, are often quite fussy about what they will or won't eat. Some eat a very small range of foods (e.g. only meat, cheese, and potato chips) and are reluctant to eat new foods. Because of all the publicity about healthy eating and the dangers of junk food, many parents worry too much about their children's eating habits, particularly if they don't eat well. Being a picky or fussy eater is not usually a problem, although it might be a nuisance. Most children go through a finicky eating stage at one time or another and it is not worth worrying too much about it unless they start losing weight.

Mealtimes should not be tense, unpleasant affairs or battlefields during which everyone becomes angry or upset. Here are some suggestions that may help you avoid arguments and ensure that your child eats a good-enough, if not perfect, diet:

- Keep only nutritious, healthy food at home. If your children want junk food, sweets or bars they will have to buy them.
- Buy and prepare the foods your children like even if this results in a monotonous diet. It is they who eat it. (You may need to cook something interesting for yourself from time to time, though.)
- Make sure they have something nutritious available to eat when they arrive home from school. This is often the time when they feel most hungry.
- Give them choices or ask for their opinion about what they want to eat.

- Don't give them money to buy fast food if they have not eaten at home.
- Avoid using food as a punishment.
- Don't worry too much about table manners. If you want to teach these to them, organise a special 'dress-up' meal once in a while. This will make table manners fun and they will not get embarrassed if they have a meal outside home.
- If you can, take your older children out to a 'proper' restaurant (not just the local pizza joint) where they can learn the etiquette of eating out: how to order a meal from the menu and what different dishes are called. In that way they will feel confident if they are invited out for a meal.

Other ways of losing weight are learned by word of mouth or the media. Most diets in magazines promise rapid weight loss (e.g. go down a dress size in a week) and are not sound nutritionally. If these diets are followed exactly, the rapid loss of weight is mainly due to loss of water. The weight is regained as rapidly as it was lost and bouts of dieting of this type result in weight cycling or yo-yo dieting that can be dangerous. Long-term research even suggests that the more diets people try, the harder it becomes for them to lose weight. Another problem associated with even moderate but frequent dieting is that nutritional needs are not met. Many young women eat almost no dairy products in an attempt to eat a low-fat diet. This means that they are not ingesting adequate amounts of calcium at a time when they should be building up bone stores to prevent osteoporosis (frail bones which are prone to fractures) in later life. Cutting out red meat can also lead to anaemia.

> *The more diets a person tries, the harder it becomes to lose weight.*

Probably the most common of the unhealthy ways of losing weight is to use cigarettes as a food substitute or to suppress appetite. While there are many reasons for teenagers starting to smoke, the reason many give for not stopping is that their weight will go up. This has serious implications for their health because up to 50 per cent of long-term smokers will die of a smoking-related illness. This makes the risks of even severe obesity pale into insignificance.

Other methods of weight control that can be dangerous include persistent fasting, self-induced vomiting, abusing laxatives and using diuretics or slimming pills. Some teenagers work out such methods by themselves while others learn about them from friends.

WHERE TO DRAW THE LINE?

A problem with dieting is where to draw the line. Many teenagers want to achieve a weight that is often too low or abnormal for them. It is difficult for the average person to know what the correct weight for a specific body height is. A simple method of determining if someone is underweight, overweight or within a healthy weight range is to use the body mass index, or BMI.

BMI is calculated by dividing a person's weight in kilos by the square of their height in metres. For example, if your child's height is 171cm and her weight is 71kg, her BMI would be 71 divided by 1.71^2 (this is equal to 71 divided by 2.92). That is, her BMI would be 24.3. A BMI of between 20 and 25 is considered a healthy weight range. For women under 16 years, the lower limit for BMI can be as low as 18.5. For younger children, before puberty, other scales should be used. It is worth noting that people are not considered medically obese until their BMI is 30 or over.

Eating disorders

The more common abnormal eating or dieting conditions are called *anorexia nervosa* and *bulimia nervosa*. Eating disorders are on the increase and seem to afflict younger and younger people. It is estimated that between 1 and 4 per cent of adolescent and young adult women suffer from eating disorders.

What causes eating disorders?

We don't yet know for sure why some people develop an eating disorder: while most teenagers diet at some stage, this becomes a serious problem in only a few of them. As always, when we don't know, theories abound. There are strong suggestions, however, that the mechanisms involved are complex: there are factors within the young persons, their families and in society at large that interact to produce this puzzling result.

WHAT HAPPENS WHEN PEOPLE STARVE?

The most telling research into starvation was done in the 1940s. It involved putting thirty-six healthy young men on a diet similar to that endured by people in concentration camps. They were conscientious objectors and the study is unlikely to be repeated because of its obvious ethical problems. These men, who were previously uninterested in dieting, became obsessed with food and eating. Some developed a preoccupation with cooking recipes, while others dreamed of food. All became lethargic, had poor concentration, lost sexual interest, were irritable, moody and could not sleep well. Four of them became depressed and one developed another psychiatric disorder. One was hospitalised for severe self-mutilation. None of these men returned to normal until normal weight had been regained. This suggests that many of the symptoms observed in people with eating disorders are likely to be the result of starvation.

Individual factors

Why does this problem afflict many more women than men? To understand this it is important to look at puberty itself. During puberty there are marked physical changes (see Chapter 1). Some, such as rapid increase in height, are similar for boys and girls; some are different. Boys' growth is more pronounced on the shoulders and they develop more muscle. This growth is often accompanied by a relative loss of weight and most boys welcome it. Girls gain width, mainly in their hips, and there is a rapid accumulation of fat when they stop growing. The typical curvaceous, pear–shaped female body and an increase in weight are the result. This is most unwelcome to young women and marks the beginning of the battle to keep thin.

Some experts believe that women with eating disorders see themselves as being fatter than they really are. Attempts to change this were a major aspect of some treatments but severe distortions in body image often improve by themselves when the young women begin eating. It was also found that most young women of normal weight think that their bodies are larger then they really are, but do not starve themselves because of it.

Other theories focus on personality traits. For example, some suggest that a sense of control is important to young women with eating disorders. They tend to be strong-willed and successful and expect their bodies to be similarly under strict control. They value self-discipline and are especially vulnerable when other areas of their life get out of control, for example when a relationship breaks up. These adolescents are capable of dieting long after other women would have given up. Another theory suggests that some young women starve themselves so that they are no longer an adult and regress to a pre-sexual body. Being an adult woman would be, for some reason, too frightening for them. While this theory has appeal, it is not supported by what women with eating disorders say about themselves.

Family factors

We can live without friends, sex or many other things. However, everyone needs to eat. Eating, providing and preparing food are essential elements in our lives and relationships, particularly family life. It is little wonder that food and eating also have strong emotional overtones. Giving food (nurturing) is often seen as an equivalent of love and care, while withdrawing food is perceived as punishment, rejection or neglect.

It is not surprising that many experts believe family factors can make dieting more likely to go out of control. On the one hand, eating disorders appear to be more frequent in some families (whether it is inherited or learned is not clear). On the other hand, conflict can crystallise around eating and become a destructive battle for control in some families. Besides, when there is parental disharmony, children can play one parent off against the other and this means that their problem is not dealt with early enough.

For example, the mother may prepare special foods and cajole the child to eat while the father wants to suspend privileges if she doesn't eat. Instead of supporting each other, they criticise each other's methods so that both approaches fail and the child continues to lose weight.

> *When an adolescent first presents with an eating disorder it is very difficult to assess the family factors that may contribute to the problem.*

Parents who are too intrusive can also aggravate eating disorders because they seek to be aware of and control everything their child does. Not eating can be a way for a child to regain some control over her life, because it is almost impossible to make someone eat.

However, when an adolescent first presents with an eating disorder it is very difficult to assess the family factors that may contribute to the problem. At that stage most families are in crisis – much more distressed, emotional and disorganised than usual. Similarly, parents with sick children may allow them less freedom and treat them as younger than they actually are because they are worried.

Parents with drug or alcohol problems are more likely to have a child with an eating disorder. The link here is that these parents often attack their children's self-esteem, even if they don't remember doing it. Their children tell of a parent who is nice to them when sober but derogatory or cruel when drunk. They may be physically or sexually abusive. In less severe cases they are verbally disparaging, lecturing their children about how stupid and useless they are. Parents may even be so intoxicated that they forget what they had said, so there is no apology or attempt to make things right afterwards.

Social factors

Having to maintain an unrealistic weight for career reasons also increases the risk of developing an eating disorder. Being a model, dancer, actor or gymnast, to give just some examples, is often incompatible with having a normal weight. Once in these occupations, dieting and abnormal eating are almost the norm.

Some women can cope with this but those who are vulnerable or who have experienced problems dieting should think very carefully about going into these or similar fields.

Anorexia nervosa

Anorexia nervosa typically starts during the middle teens. The teenager tends to be quiet, hard-working and close to her family. Her adolescence has often gone smoothly. She may be a little overweight or her weight may be normal but at some stage she starts to diet. This may be in response to teasing about her weight or to education at school about the dangers of obesity or a high-fat diet. She may have been recently unwell and temporarily lost her appetite. She may be under stress due to exams or a family crisis.

She continues dieting and starts avoiding more foods. High-fat foods are the first to go, often followed by sweets and red meat. She may start skipping meals or refusing to eat with her family. Her weight continues to fall. At first her parents may compliment her on her discipline and the moderate loss of weight. At some stage, however, her family or friends notice her loss of weight, begin to worry about her and say something. Many will stop dieting at this point. Some keep going.

Periods usually stop when the proportion of fat in the body falls below a critical level.

Her periods will stop if she persists with dieting. This usually happens when the proportion of fat in the body falls below a critical level but it can occur earlier, shortly after the beginning of the dieting. She is not concerned about this; in fact, she is often glad not to have periods. In spite of the loss of weight she continues exercising: doing hundreds of sit-ups a day or jogging. When she eats something, even a very small amount, she feels guilty and thinks that her stomach is full and sticks out. She is then compelled to burn the kilojoules she ate by doing exercise. Although she does not eat, she is concerned about food and may prepare meals or bake cakes for the rest of the family. She hides her thinness by wearing loose, baggy dresses and long sleeves. She avoids going out with friends, becomes irritable and moody. However, her marks at school are still unaffected. Her parents or friends are shocked when they accidentally see her partially undressed, noticing she is just skin and bones.

If the weight loss continues, she will show physical symptoms including sensitivity to cold, lack of energy and dizziness with sudden changes of posture. Fine downy hair, called lanugo, may begin to grow over her body. These symptoms are the same as those shown by people suffering from starvation. She may still say that she is overweight and try to lose more weight. By now, her family and friends are attempting to persuade or force her to eat, even to the point of fighting with her. Mealtimes are full of arguments, pleading, fights and tears. Everyone sees her as totally preoccupied with food and dieting, even to the point of being irrational. At this stage her family probably insists that she seek help and she may go, often unwillingly, to her local doctor or for counselling. She still maintains that she is fine and that everyone is worrying unnecessarily.

Once the existence of the problem becomes clear some young women start a career of deceit and lies. They lie to cover up their not eating or to justify not going out with friends or to parties, because this often involves eating or going to restaurants. They begin exercising in secret, taking laxatives and hiding food. If parents force them to eat, they may vomit afterwards. Food and dieting become their main preoccupation while they increasingly become socially isolated and difficult to live with.

The picture described is the typical history of a restricting anorexic. These teenagers try to lose weight mainly by reducing the amount of food they eat. They also eat a very limited number of foods (e.g. bran, black coffee, wholemeal bread, salad and apples).

About half of these patients have eating binges, often followed by self-induced vomiting, interspersed with dieting. However, what they call a 'binge' is frequently quite different from what most people understand a binge is.

How frequent is this problem?

Eating disorders have become more common since the middle of the twentieth century. Before then, the most common reason given for weight loss was self-starvation for religious devotion. Recent studies suggest that around one teenage girl in a hundred suffers from anorexia nervosa. Some groups that are more vulnerable, such as female ballet dancers, have much higher rates of the condition. Anorexia nervosa is rare in boys.

Less severe forms are more frequent, and the boundaries between this condition and exaggerated forms of dieting are vague. Dieting and other weight reduction measures are extremely common. The issue is when such habits become abnormal. This is clear in extreme cases but there are many others, less severe, that go undetected.

Sarah felt that she was expected to do well, like her older sister who was studying law and getting excellent marks. She had heard her father talking often about how much he had wanted to go to university and how he couldn't because his family was poor. It had been a disappointment for him although he was a successful businessman. Year 11 was more difficult than she had expected. To make things worse, she had also broken up with her boyfriend. The reason had been a trivial argument after her birthday – her sixteenth – but they had been growing apart for some weeks. Sarah started thinking that maybe if she had been slimmer and more attractive they would not have split up. One innocent comment he had made about her buttocks was intensely clear in her memory. She started skipping meals and exercising for at least an hour a day to lose weight.

Initially, Sarah's sisters (she also had a younger sister) and friends were impressed by the changes she had made. Her parents had always eaten healthily and were pleased to see her give up junk food. Her friends complimented her as her size 10 jeans became loose. She became more driven and was working harder at school.

However, as Sarah continued losing weight, her parents became worried, particularly when her mother found out she had lost her periods. Her mother reacted by spending a lot of time with Sarah, preparing her favourite foods and cajoling her to eat. Sarah's father tried to force her to eat and her older sister alternated between concern and annoyance, retreating into her studies. Mealtimes became a nightmare. Sarah began wrapping herself in many layers of clothes but still shivered. She became irritable and her family sometimes found her sobbing for no apparent reason.

Finally, when she ran up the stairs at home and fainted, cutting her forehead on the banister, her parents insisted on taking her to the doctor.

When Sarah was assessed she was eating extremely small amounts of food and her BMI was 14. She could see few good things about herself. She felt she would never fulfil her parents' expectations. However, the control and determination she had needed to lose weight made her feel special. She had succeeded where many others had failed. She was terrified that if she gave up dieting she would become an obese failure.

Her parents were worried and on edge. They could not understand what they had done wrong. They didn't care about Sarah's school marks, only wanted her to be happy and have a normal life. Her mother had stayed at home precisely to ensure their daughters were well looked after. They shared many activities as a family and her father, although busy, had not allowed his work to take too much of his time. They were puzzled about precisely why Sarah, who had been the most considerate and thoughtful of their three daughters, could do this to herself. They blamed themselves because, although both had known about anorexia, they had not realised earlier the seriousness of Sarah's condition and done something about it.

Anorexia before puberty

While anorexia nervosa usually starts after puberty, girls as young as 9 or 10 years can suffer from it. The manifestations are much the same. Besides other complications, these children can stop growing because adequate nutrition is necessary for growth to occur.

Anorexia in males

Eating disorders are rare in men, about one male for every ten to fifteen females. The numbers are smaller but the symptoms are much the same. However, young men are dieting more and some find that their dieting gets out of control. There are occupations for boys, such as in the performing arts or as a jockey, that increase the risk of eating disorders.

Almost by accident – he had a cholesterol test on one of those health promotion days – Branko found that he had a high blood cholesterol level. He was 12 years of age. It turned out that his father also had the same problem and was found to have heart disease. Branko was told that high cholestorol could be bad for his heart. After doing some research on the Internet, he decided to start a low-fat diet. He thought that this would encourage his family to eat healthier food and thus would also be good for his father. Branko stuck firmly to the diet but, unfortunately, lost too much weight and became unwell. He lost sight of his original reason for eating carefully and started refusing all his mother's food. He then became a strict vegetarian.

Branko was 14 years old when he came for treatment. By then he was very thin (his BMI was 15) and he needed two admissions to hospital for refeeding (weight restoration). Even after discharge it was very difficult to get him to eat. Only the threat of hospitalisation persuaded him to keep his weight near the recommended minimum.

Much time was spent teaching Branko and his parents about food that was not fattening but that provided adequate nutrition. He felt fat when he was actually very skinny. The two years he had spent obsessed with food and dieting meant he had been left behind academically. He had also lost contact with his friends, who did not share his obsession.

He decided to join a gym and get fit, which meant that he had to eat enough to develop muscle. The supervisor in the gym was told of his trouble with eating and insisted that he eat an adequate diet if he were to train there. Branko trained hard but did not overdo it and managed to maintain his weight. This produced results and he was proud of his new physique. His new image and confidence helped him regain contact with his friends and be accepted by them.

Two years later, Branko was doing well academically and socially. He had maintained a healthy weight and felt happy. Unfortunately, he had stopped growing and was shorter than expected. Investigation suggested that the period spent underweight had reduced his potential height. He still was quite fastidious with his food and very conscious of his body shape.

What happens when anorexia is not treated?

Most of the information available refers to the more serious cases treated in specialised clinics and it is unclear whether other, less severe, cases have a similar outcome.

What happens in the long term varies a lot from sufferer to sufferer. Untreated anorexia nervosa tends to become chronic. Up to 20 per cent of treated patients with severe anorexia die in the following twenty years, the majority because of starvation, complications of the illness (e.g. infections, problems with the chemical composition of the blood produced by the dieting or vomiting) or suicide. It is common for these women to be depressed, sometimes severely so. Some develop obsessions or compulsions (see Chapter 9). They are constantly preoccupied with thoughts of food and dieting. They have difficulties making or keeping friends and may not marry. Some abuse alcohol or other drugs.

How do I know if my child has anorexia nervosa?

You should seriously suspect that your daughter has anorexia nervosa if she has the following symptoms:

- She has lost weight to below the minimum for her age and height (a BMI below 17.5).
- She is afraid of becoming fat despite being underweight. Sometimes this is difficult to find out because she may deny it. Tell-tale signs you can notice, however, include her comments or if she weighs herself frequently.
- She thinks she is too fat or believes that being so thin is not abnormal, or she is preoccupied with the shape of her body, believing her belly, thighs or buttocks are too fat, in spite of her being very thin.
- Her periods have stopped for at least three cycles (this only applies to women after puberty). It is difficult to detect this symptom in women who are taking the contraceptive pill, which induces the periods.

> *Identifying the problem early offers the best chance for treatment and may even avoid the development of a full-blown disorder.*

For males the symptoms are the same except the one referring to periods.

You don't need to wait until the symptoms have reached the stage of a full-blown illness to seek help. As with other emotional disorders, detecting the problem early offers the best chance for treatment and may even avoid the development of the illness. Parents of teenage girls need to be discreetly vigilant about this potential problem.

The best indication of a problem is a BMI below the normal range (below 20). It is a good idea to keep an eye on your child's weight rather than her eating (eating can be quite capricious in teenagers and some kind of dieting is very frequent).

You need to be particularly observant if she decides to become vegetarian or if she takes up strict diets. This can be more dangerous if it happens during times of stress or after important life crises.

Where can I go to seek help?

Because anorexia nervosa is a complex disorder and often becomes chronic, it requires comprehensive treatment. A central aspect of this is the medical management, and so I would recommend that you consult a psychiatrist experienced in the treatment of this condition. Alternatively, find out about centres that specialise in the treatment of eating disorders (there are units in most capital cities) and request an assessment in one of them.

The main problem will be convincing your child that she needs help. The first step is to gently confront her with your worries. It is good to be specific and suggest what you would like to do. For example, you could say that you have noticed that she looks pale, is lacking in energy and seems to be feeling the cold badly. She may deny this. Emphasise that you are worried about her weight and would like her to see the family doctor. Enlist the help of relatives or friends. Let your doctor know that you are concerned about her weight loss and the possibility of an eating disorder and seek referral to a specialist.

During the first visit your doctor may check the teenager's pulse, which may be slow, and measure her blood pressure. Blood tests will be necessary also. These may include a full blood count (looking for anaemia) and serum electrolytes (to verify the level of potassium, which is affected by vomiting and can cause heart problems). It is unhelpful, however, to get bogged down with endless tests looking for obscure physical causes when she keeps on losing weight. Investigations, if necessary, can be done at the same time as a psychiatric evaluation or as a part of it.

Treating anorexia nervosa

The standard treatment of anorexia nervosa has three components:

- Weight restoration, also called refeeding. Most experts agree that the *first goal* should be to achieve a minimum healthy weight. This is because regaining a healthy weight often results in an improvement in mood, a reduction in the obsession with food and dieting, and positive personality changes.
- Family therapy. The young woman and her family need to be engaged in treatment from the very beginning. The younger the teenager, the more important is the role of the family. Initially, the therapy will concentrate on education about the illness. Later it will move on to finding out how parents and siblings can help the young woman maintain a healthy weight or make this task easier for her.
- Individual counselling or psychotherapy is also important. It will focus initially on explaining her condition to the teenager and giving her nutritional advice. Later, when her weight has reached a more normal level (people who are starving do not benefit much from counselling), therapy may focus on other issues, such as helping her manage stress or deal with conflict.

Two other important aspects of the treatment plan are the choice of a target weight and to decide the best way to administer the treatment (in hospital or as out-patient).

> *The first goal of treatment should be to achieve a minimum healthy weight.*

The target weight

The target weight is the weight to be achieved through the weight restoration program. Ideally, it should be a weight that would allow for her periods to resume and for her to take up normal and healthy activities once again. The return of the periods is the best indication that a minimum healthy weight has been reached. This target should be discussed with the teenager and her parents and a weight agreed upon. The target weight, apart from providing a concrete goal, emphasises that the focus is on weight gain and not on eating. Eating is only a means to achieve normal weight and nutrition.

The treatment setting

There are two main reasons for admitting an adolescent with an eating disorder to hospital. The first is because she is in substantial physical danger. This will be either because she is so underweight that she is no longer able to manage normal activities such as school without risk or because she has complications, such as a low level of potassium in the blood or an abnormal electrocardiogram suggesting that her heart is not working properly. The second reason is that out-patient treatment is not being effective and she is either not gaining weight or continuing to lose it. The threat of hospitalisation is often a lever to encourage patients to gain weight.

Admission to hospital should ideally be to a ward that has staff with the expertise to run a program for anorexia nervosa. The program will typically revolve around a clear expectation of weight gain, with appropriate meals being served under supervision, and a supervised time after meals to prevent vomiting. If the agreed weight gain is not achieved, the patient's level of activity is restricted, for instance by having to remain in bed. As she gains weight she is allowed more activities and more freedom. Therefore, both positive (privileges such as visitors, mild exercise, praise) and negative (bed rest, loss of privileges) reinforcements are used.

Supportive psychotherapy is used simultaneously: initially to encourage a return to health and later to understand the worries behind the weight loss. Group therapy can be useful as these teenagers will often accept confrontation of their self-defeating habits from each other, but not from professionals. Because hospitalisation may last several weeks, it is important to organise school work for teenagers who are still at school so that their schooling does not suffer too much.

Discharge takes place after achieving the target weight but treatment should continue. Actually, the weeks after discharge are particularly important and teenagers and families require a good deal of support during this transition. The aim of this part of the treatment is weight maintenance to prevent relapse, and to stop the development of other abnormal habits such as bingeing or vomiting.

FORCE-FEEDING

Most experts agree that force-feeding is not the solution for anorexia nervosa. Nevertheless, feeding through a naso-gastric tube or parenteral nutrition may be required in rare circumstances when there is risk of death.

In naso-gastric feeding, a fine plastic tube is introduced through the nose until it reaches the stomach (this is a simple and not particularly unpleasant procedure). Liquefied food is then passed to the stomach through the tube. Total parenteral nutrition is a more delicate technique that consists of injecting nutrients directly into the bloodstream through an intravenous line.

These procedures have risks and present ethical and legal dilemmas, particularly if the young woman continues refusing to eat. However, some severely starved patients prefer naso-gastric tube feeding to eating, at least initially.

Is medication useful?

Many drugs have been tried in the treatment of anorexia nervosa without much success. Medication has a limited role in the treatment of this disorder, although there are exceptions. Medication is useful when an adolescent has anorexia as well as another mental disorder, such as obsessive compulsive disorder or depression. If the other condition benefits from treatment with medication, then drug treatment is indicated. Another exception is when anorexia is not typical but a look-alike. That is, if fasting and weight loss are in fact the manifestation of another condition, for example a teenager with schizophrenia may refuse to eat because she believes that food is poisoned. Although superficially it looks like it, this is not true anorexia and it will benefit from the treatment of schizophrenia. Medication should be used with caution in teenagers with anorexia. Their low weight and poor nutritional state increase the risk of side effects.

> *Medication has a limited role in the treatment of anorexia nervosa.*

How effective is treatment?

The short-term results of treatment are very good: around 90 per cent of patients successfully regain their target weight. However, four years later, only half will have maintained a healthy weight and have regular periods. Of the other 50 per cent, half still have substantial eating problems with weight below normal. The other half shows fewer difficulties but has ongoing low weight or other eating problems. Many women in this group remain preoccupied with food, dieting and body image.

In summary, outcome is worse in women who:

- have reached a very low weight before treatment
- are older (more than 18 years) when they develop the illness
- have had previous unsuccessful treatment
- have disturbed family relationships
- vomit and purge.

Bulimia nervosa

Bulimia can develop in young women who previously had anorexia. However, the majority of cases occur in women who are trying to diet but are of normal weight. They skip meals or reduce their food intake to totally inadequate levels. As a result of being ravenous they begin to lose control of their eating and binge. They find out about vomiting from their friends or the media and try it out. If they are successful, they eat larger amounts and vomit.

A BINGE

A binge is when the person eats an inordinate amount of food – much more than most people would eat in similar circumstances – during a short period, usually less than two hours. This excludes social situations in which large amounts of food are consumed, such as during celebrations. Continuous snacking on small amounts of food through the day is not considered a binge. However, an episode of binge-eating can start in one place (e.g. a restaurant) and continue somewhere else (e.g. at home). Sufferers often describe a feeling of frenzy and loss of control during these binges.

The type of food consumed during a binge varies from person to person. It is common, however, to eat large amounts of pre-prepared foods that do not require much chewing, such as ice cream, cake or other high-calorie, sweet foods.

After an episode of overeating and vomiting they feel ashamed, guilty and keep it secret. The next day they often exercise, use laxatives or fast at breakfast and lunch to compensate for the overeating. By early evening, however, they are starving again and may binge. This pattern can become a strong habit, like an addiction. Once bingeing gets out of control these young women can consume huge amounts of food in a short period, sometimes even frozen or uncooked food. Families may find the fridge or cupboards empty. Some teenagers can spend all their pocket money, or even all the money they have earned in a part-time job, on food.

Young women with bulimia typically have a normal weight.

One important difference with anorexia nervosa is that young women with bulimia typically have a normal weight. At most, they are slightly underweight or overweight. Bulimia sufferers are older than anorexia sufferers.

Overeating and vomiting are seldom the only problems. Other symptoms, such as moodiness and periods of depression or self-loathing, are common. These teenagers may be impulsive in other areas of their life or self-mutilate. Problems with alcohol or other drugs occur in about one-third of the sufferers. Relationships with their friends are often affected.

A person with bulimia can have a normal weight and still be quite unwell because frequent vomiting can produce serious health problems. Vomiting reduces the amount of potassium in the blood and causes other imbalances. The stomach acid can wear the teeth away and repeated self-induced vomiting may cause stomach bleeding.

How do I know if my daughter has bulimia nervosa?

You should suspect that your daughter may have bulimia nervosa if she shows the following problems for several months:

- episodes of binge eating followed by inappropriate compensatory actions to prevent gaining weight (e.g. vomiting, taking laxatives or diuretics, fasting, overexercising)
- her opinion of herself is influenced too much by the shape and weight of her body.

Because people with bulimia feel ashamed, they try to conceal their binges and become secretive. As they have a normal weight there are few clues to make you suspect that something might be wrong, particularly if your daughter is not living at home. Some telltale signs are:

- spending a lot of money on food
- being too concerned about weight
- taking up fasting or radical diets that are followed for only a few days at a time
- doing spasmodic, frantic exercise while ignoring work commitments or social activities
- becoming increasingly isolated, moody and erratic
- hoarding or hiding food, food scraps or laxatives in unusual places, such as in drawers with clothes
- having teeth, particularly the front teeth, that have deteriorated (e.g. chipped) without a reason.

How frequent is bulimia nervosa?

Bulimia is a problem identified only recently as a mental disorder. It was first written about in the 1970s when it was seen as a rare condition. It has become clear since then that it is common.

About one in a hundred women of senior high-school age has bulimia and it is being seen increasingly in younger teenagers. The figures for boys are probably a tenth or less that of girls. Milder versions of this syndrome are more frequent. In the United States 5 per cent of female college students admit to bingeing regularly and then vomiting or using laxatives to get rid of the food.

Becky, who was 17, had been very overweight as a young teenager. The year before she had gone on a very strict diet and lost 20 kg. She had started feeling good about herself, felt attractive and received many compliments. However, it was hard for her to maintain that weight. She found that when she ate the meals prepared by her mother she began to put on weight. Becky then started skipping meals. She got into a pattern of not eating breakfast or lunch and found this kept her weight down, but she felt ravenous when she came home from school. When hungry, Becky began eating anything that she could find. This became a frantic swallowing of food that she did not even have the time to chew. One day, after one of the binges Becky felt sick and vomited. That made her feel relieved, empty and much better. She then started inducing vomiting after these binges. This got rid of the food but her binges then became larger and more frequent.

Becky became moody and cranky, she was arguing more with her mother and sister (she was the middle child and oldest girl), who were mystified by the disappearance of tubs of ice cream, biscuits and cakes. Becky's family was rather volatile but the real fireworks began when her mother found out Becky was vomiting after meals she had cooked especially for her. They were revolted by the traces of vomit in the bathroom that Becky had failed to clean. The rest of the family were worried, angry and could not understand Becky's behaviour. After one particularly bad fight with her parents Becky left home to stay with friends.

When Becky and her family came for assessment, they could barely be in the same room together as there was so much anger, resentment and recrimination. Becky complained about her parents' intrusiveness, high expectations and failure to let her grow up. Her parents complained about Becky's defiance and lack of willingness to help herself ('How can she destroy herself doing these stupid things?'). Her father blamed her mother because of her nagging, quick temper and criticism of Becky. Her mother blamed her father for his lack of support ('You spend the whole week at work and don't care about me or your children') and his indulging Becky.

When seen on her own, Becky expressed a deep self-hatred and despair. She realised that her life was falling apart but could not help herself. She felt that she had lost control of her eating completely and was terrified of regaining weight and becoming fat again. She confessed that she was so angry and frustrated at times that she had begun to cut herself about her arms with a razor blade until she bled. The sight of the blood was often a release, like a catharsis.

Initially, treatment concentrated on improving her eating habits (she was to have several small meals and snacks each day) and on reducing her vomiting. She had an added incentive to achieve this when blood tests showed that her potassium level was so low that her heart could stop beating. In later sessions Becky was able to say that her mother had been very violent to her. This was discussed in family meetings in spite of the shame, guilt and embarrassment it caused to everyone. This problem (the mother's volatile and aggressive character and her hitting the children, particularly Becky, when she had been drinking) had been a family secret. Becky's father was regretful that he had kept the secret, even to the extent of lying to doctors about cuts and bruises when Becky was a child. He knew that his wife needed help but had not dared to suggest it. However, the time had come. He and his wife agreed to see a therapist, seeking help for her drinking and the problems in their marriage.

Gradually, the situation at home improved, as did Becky's bingeing and vomiting. Becky was also feeling happier, less

> moody and was regaining some control and sense of direction in her life. A few months later she went to university and left home to live in a residential college. By then her life seemed to have almost returned to normal. She had lingering concerns about being attractive and becoming fat.

Treating bulimia nervosa

The basic principles of treatment for bulimia nervosa are similar to those used in the treatment of anorexia nervosa, with the

> *Breaking the cycle of bingeing and vomiting is the main goal of treatment.*

difference that breaking the cycle of bingeing and vomiting replaces weight restoration. As with anorexia nervosa, it is important that treatment is given by a professional experienced in these disorders and fully aware of the potential medical complications. This requires, at least, working in close association with a medical practitioner such as the family doctor.

Most experts agree that out-patient treatment is the best option for bulimia. This will require frequent appointments at the beginning. In younger teenagers, a combination of individual and family therapy is ideal. In older adolescents and young adults, the initial approach is usually individual. Group therapy can also be a helpful adjunct for sufferers with chronic bulimia.

Everyone needs to be aware that bulimia has usually been present for months, if not years, before treatment starts so that, more often than not, it is a well-established habit. Improvement, therefore, will take time and expecting success overnight is unrealistic and likely to lead to more anger and disappointment.

The way to stop bingeing is by eating small, balanced, regular meals: ideally, three small meals and three snacks a day. Attempts to lose weight should stop until bingeing is under control. Another useful strategy in some adolescents is gradually to add sensible, regular exercise. This is helpful not only for keeping their bodies in shape and allowing them to eat more without putting on weight, but also for providing a healthy outlet for distressing emotions.

Some therapists ask the teenager to keep a diary to record what she eats and when she vomits. In this way they may find that there are danger periods for bingeing, often associated with emotions such as anger, boredom or loneliness. They can then work out ways to deal with these feelings, for example by asking family or friends for specific support such as not having danger foods stored in the fridge.

Not surprisingly, the situation at home is often out of control. Frequently the house is in turmoil (everyone in the family is watching the young woman, there are arguments when food is missing, there is mistrust, recriminations) and this is not helpful for her or the rest of the family. For example, it is helpful to agree that, if she does vomit, she should leave the bathroom clean or, if she binges on someone else's food, she should replace it. Working with the family can concentrate initially on such concrete issues.

Because bulimia is a chronic problem and relapses are frequent, treatment also needs to continue for lengthy periods. This is made more necessary because many bulimic teenagers have ongoing personality problems and rigid, unhealthy patterns of coping and relating to people.

Hospitalisation

In-patient treatment is not necessary for bulimia. Bulimia is a condition where lasting results are only obtained with lifestyle changes. It is comparatively easy to reduce vomiting by supervision while in hospital. However, changes typically don't persist at home, where it is impossible to bar access to the fridge or bathroom.

Hospital admission is used only when an adolescent develops physical complications that can endanger her life, becomes acutely suicidal or when intensive out-patient treatment has failed. In these circumstances the admission is brief, rarely exceeding two or three weeks. In-patient treatment is not useful to treat someone who is uncooperative or who lacks motivation: she will relapse as soon as she returns home.

Is medication helpful?

Contrary to the case with anorexia nervosa, medication can be a helpful complement in the treatment of bulimia sufferers, although

> *Medication can be a helpful aspect of treatment in bulimia.*

it is not a substitute for psychotherapy and education. The antidepressant drugs (SSRIs) mentioned in Chapter 6 are helpful in the reduction of the number of binges. The reason for this is not known and relapse is frequent when the medication is stopped.

What are the results of treatment?

There are few studies of bulimia sufferers over long periods. Bulimia usually starts in the late teenage years and one-third of these teenagers improve without treatment. About 70 per cent of those treated get better with out-patient treatment. The outlook is less positive when hospital admission is required. A substantial number of these women continue having phases during which they binge and vomit.

Complications of eating disorders that appear years later

It is worth mentioning some problems that may surface years later, even in women who have overcome their eating disorder. The first is the increased risk of osteoporosis, which results in fragile bones and fractures, if the young woman had been without periods for a year or longer. This is because of the small amounts of dairy products – and, therefore, the low amount of calcium – that most women with anorexia eat. Another problem is infertility, especially if weight remains low. If conception does occur, these women have a higher frequency of miscarriage and of having very low-weight babies.

It can also be very difficult for women with a chronic eating disorder (or those who have recovered only partially) to adequately feed their own children. They often have distorted ideas of how much food a small child needs or serve a very low-fat diet, inappropriate for a small child.

What can I do to help my daughter?

When your daughter is first starting to lose weight it is useful to reassure her that you think she looks fine and encourage her to be cautious. Even for overweight teenagers, increasing exercise and eating healthier food is a safer and more effective way to lose weight than dieting. In particular, discourage your child from following crash diets.

If this doesn't work and she becomes too thin, she needs to be persuaded she needs help as soon as possible. Your family doctor and the school counsellor can advise and help you in this regard. Once help has been organised, it is useful for both parents to be available if asked by the therapist. This gives a strong message to your child that you are both very concerned about her. The problem can usually be solved more quickly if both parents say the same things.

Once treatment has started, it is important to follow the therapist's advice. If you disagree with the advice or find it impossible to follow it, discuss this directly with the therapist and come to a compromise. If compromise can't be reached or you think that treatment is not working (e.g. your daughter continues losing weight), ask for a second opinion.

You may need to do things that your daughter doesn't like, such as restricting her level of exercise. This is preferable to letting her participate in activities such as playing netball when she is so thin and sick she may collapse. However, this will depend on your daughter's age, because it is easier and more appropriate to ask a 12-year-old not to do something than an 18-year-old.

Families may need to strongly encourage their daughter to go into hospital if she is very underweight, even if they will miss her terribly.

When an eating disorder has become more chronic, especially in an older teenager, sometimes parents need to pull away a little. They can express their concern and be available if needed, but they should let their daughter manage her own eating problems. This can be difficult at first but may be necessary to help her take control of her own life.

What can I do to help prevent some of these problems?

You have already seen that there are many factors in society that make young women more vulnerable to eating problems. These are difficult to change at a family or individual level and so what you can actually do is limited. Some healthy eating habits and a good relationship with your child, however, can help prevent these problems.

- It is helpful to eat a reasonably healthy diet.
- Make food and eating enjoyable and avoid arguments at the meal table.
- Don't criticise your child's body shape in a negative, demeaning way (e.g. calling her 'fatty' or other names).
- Be a good role model for your child: if a girl's mother is constantly talking about her weight and following the latest crash diet, the daughter will see this as a model of how she should behave. Children also pick up the way their families talk about their bodies and it is helpful for them in accepting themselves if they see that their parents accept their own bodies.
- Be aware that modelling, ballet and similar occupations carry with them a substantial risk. Teenagers interested in such professions need to be monitored carefully.
- Family involvement in fun activities that include physical exercise or sport is helpful.
- Encourage your child to participate in a variety of activities so she finds where she fits in best. Some may not achieve in areas in which their parents want them to excel. Forcing them to keep on trying may make them feel a failure.
- If you find out that other adults, such as gymnastics coaches or dance teachers, suggest that your child should diet to an inappropriate weight, you should intervene. You may need to organise a different coach or dance teacher to protect your child. It may even be useful to ask if eating disorders are a problem in that particular school or coaching group.

In summary, though outside systems may have values that put people at risk of eating disorders, parents have the power to reduce these effects.

13 Tangled thoughts, strange ideas

This chapter takes you through the psychotic disorders, particularly schizophrenia. This is a severe illness that afflicts people in the prime of their life and often becomes chronic. There are effective treatments to help sufferers, though not a cure. It is essential that these young people receive treatment as early as possible.

Psychosis

There are many meanings for the word 'psychosis'. The most widely used is a mental condition in which the person has lost touch with reality. That is, individuals become unable to decide if what they see, hear, think or feel is real or not. However, the term does not apply to minor distortions of reality that involve relative judgment.

> **Hallucinations or delusions are the hallmarks of psychosis.**

For example, no one would consider a beautiful woman who thinks she is not attractive or people who underestimate their achievements to be psychotic. When people are psychotic, they usually have hallucinations or delusions, or both. These experiences are the hallmarks of psychosis.

232

When someone begins to experience hallucinations and delusions we say that person is suffering a psychotic episode (this is often called a 'breakdown').

DELUSIONS

Delusions are *false beliefs*. The deluded person is firmly convinced of something against everyone else's opinion and when there is no evidence to suggest it is true. For example, a man may be sure that Martians are controlling the thoughts in his brain through laser beams. This person is so convinced of this that he walks around with a hat made of aluminium foil to reflect these non-existent beams and won't change his mind in spite of the most logical arguments. The main characteristic of delusions is the sense of certainty with which they are held by the person experiencing them, no matter how bizarre or strange they may seem to everyone else.

The more common types of delusions are:

- *persecutory*, in which the person believes himself to be persecuted, attacked or harassed (these are also called paranoid delusions)
- *of reference*, in which the person believes newspapers, television or radio broadcasts make reference, usually in a pejorative way, to him
- *of being controlled*, when the person believes his thoughts, feelings or impulses are not his own but imposed by something or someone else, as in the above example
- *grandiose*, when the person has an exaggerated sense of his own importance, power or identity, for example one woman believed her parents were not her real parents but that she was a love child of Queen Elizabeth II, while another woman believed she was Anastasia Romanova, the daughter of the last Russian tsar
- *of jealousy*, when the person has an irrational belief that his partner is unfaithful, for example a middle-aged man might conclude that his wife was having an affair with a neighbour from the way cars were parked in the street
- *bizarre*, when the person has absurd and bizarre beliefs, such as being convinced that his dentist has installed an electronic device in his tooth which allows the CIA to control his thoughts.

HALLUCINATIONS

Hallucinations are *false perceptions*: sensory experiences without an actual stimulation of the relevant sensory organ. Examples include hearing people talking when there is no one there; seeing people, animals or objects when they are not present; smelling non-existent smells; or tasting non-existent flavours. To the person experiencing them hallucinatory episodes are as real as if someone was actually there or spoke; hallucinations cannot be distinguished from true perceptions. Hallucinations are described by the relevant sensory organ: olfactory hallucination means a hallucination of taste; auditory hallucination means a hallucination of sound, and so on.

Types of psychotic episode

Psychotic episodes can be caused by many medical problems, from illnesses of the brain, such as tumours, to infections, such as encephalitis and AIDS, to intoxication with drugs. Because of this, it is often difficult to find out what type of psychotic episode is occurring when someone is experiencing this problem for the first time. What happens during the following weeks or months is important to clarify this. The most common types of psychotic episode are:

• *Drug-induced psychosis.* This is a frequent cause of psychotic symptoms in adolescents. They are produced by intoxication with alcohol or drugs such as amphetamines, LSD or marijuana (see Chapter 14). Drug-induced psychoses improve quickly, in a few days, as the drugs disappear from the body. It is not unusual, however, for adolescents to continue showing symptoms of psychosis and to develop an illness such as schizophrenia. It is difficult to know in these cases whether the drug triggered the illness in a person who was susceptible or whether the illness was already there and the abuse of drugs just made it more noticeable.

- *Schizophrenia.* This is a condition in which symptoms have been present for longer. It is described in more detail on the next page.
- *Bipolar disorder or manic-depressive illness.* Teenagers with this mood disorder can present with psychotic symptoms as well. This condition has been described in Chapter 7.
- *Schizoaffective disorder.* This is an uncommon illness in which adolescents show symptoms of both schizophrenia and bipolar disorder (depression or mania).
- *Psychotic depression.* Young people with this severe form of depression have hallucinations and delusions as well as depressive symptoms. Their delusions are of a depressive nature (e.g. a teenager who was convinced he had done something terrible and was going to be thrown into hell for it).
- *Brief reactive psychosis.* Some people who go through an accumulation of crises or major life changes – a death in the family, severe pressure at school – can develop psychotic symptoms in an acute form. Often these episodes settle quickly, after a few days.
- *Organic psychosis.* In this condition psychotic symptoms appear as part of a physical illness (e.g. children can have hallucinations when they have a high fever). Organic psychosis can be the manifestation of illnesses that interfere with the functioning of the brain such as tumours or encephalitis. In these cases there are other symptoms as well, such as disorientation (the person doesn't know where he is or the date) and loss of memory.

> *Because psychosis has many forms, the duration of the illness, treatment and whether the person is cured or not varies from case to case.*

Because psychosis has many forms, the duration of the illness, treatment and whether the person is cured or not varies from case to case. Psychotic episodes may last for hours, days, weeks or years, depending on the cause. Most of these episodes are of relatively short duration and most people recover completely from the experience. More than three in a hundred people will experience a significant psychotic episode at some time in their lives.

A psychotic episode is a serious medical illness that can be effectively treated. However, as in all mental disorders, it is important to detect and treat it early. If your teenage child shows any of these symptoms you should consult your doctor as soon as possible. Most psychotic episodes in adolescents are caused by schizophrenia or drug-induced psychoses.

Schizophrenia

Schizophrenia manifests itself in a variety of disturbances of thinking, feelings and the way in which the adolescent behaves and relates to the outside world. It always results in impairment in the functioning of the young person and personality change.

The manifestations of schizophrenia are divided into three groups.

- *Positive symptoms.* These reflect an excess or distortion of normal psychological functions:
  - *Hallucinations.* Most typical are auditory hallucinations (hearing one or several voices, usually running a pejorative commentary on the sufferer's actions, talking in the third person about the sufferer in a denigrating way, and so on). Isolated experiences such as hearing one's name being called are not considered a symptom of this condition. Hallucinations in younger children are almost impossible to distinguish from a vivid imagination (e.g. talking to an imaginary friend) and are quite normal. Other forms of hallucinations, such as foul smells or strange tastes, can also occur
  - *Delusions.* See the box on Page 233.
  - *Disorganised speech* (which reflects disorganised thinking). The normal thought processes and logic are often faulty in individuals with schizophrenia. Their train of thought may be difficult to follow because they jump from one topic to another, give unrelated answers to questions, invent new words or use words with idiosyncratic meanings.
  - *Disorganised motor behaviour.* The most typical form of this is catatonia: the sufferer maintains a rigid, occasionally bizarre,

posture and resists efforts to be moved. Occasionally, he can become extremely excited or agitated.

- *Negative symptoms.* These reflect a loss or deterioration of normal psychological functions:
  - *Diminished emotional responsiveness.* The face is immobile, unresponsive, with poor eye contact or shows a very limited range of emotions. Sufferers often comment they feel strange and cut off from the world outside. They seem turned inwards and preoccupied with their own experiences. Now and then, their feelings or behaviour are inappropriate (e.g. giggles or laughs in situations in which being serious is the right thing to do; grimacing or posturing).
  - *Lack of motivation.* The sufferer has no willpower, drive, ability to carry through activities or decisions, or has difficulty making his mind up. These people may sit for long periods, appear lethargic and show little interest in what is going on. They may take a long time to make decisions or may change their mind often in a short period of time.

- *Deterioration in the level of functioning.* Teenagers with schizophrenia show a drop in their performance at school or work. Their ability to relate to relatives and peers, self-care and hygiene decline, compared with what they were before the onset of the illness. This can be difficult to establish, at least initially, in young adolescents and can be easily mistaken for normal teenage behaviour. Many parents think this is just 'a stage' the child is going through.

For adolescents to be diagnosed as suffering from schizophrenia they must have shown symptoms for at least six months and have had manifestations of each of the three groups of symptoms (positive, negative, and deterioration of functioning). It is also necessary to exclude mood disorders, drug-induced psychosis and physical illness that could account for the symptoms. This can sometimes prove difficult in the short term. When symptoms are present for less than six months the condition is called *schizophreniform psychosis*.

The stages of schizophrenia

This illness usually starts during the teenage years or during the twenties. It has three phases that vary in length from person to person. These are:

- *Prodromal stage.* It is characterised by a gradual appearance of the symptoms. Teenagers' performance at school declines, they lose interest and motivation in activities previously enjoyed, withdraw into themselves and gradually lose friends. They may spend a lot of time in bed; their care for their appearance and grooming diminishes. Friends and relatives notice the change. Often the teenagers have odd ideas or interests (e.g. the occult, extrasensory perception). They may feel strange or different, as if something is going on and they don't know what. Similar changes, however, can be observed in many teenagers who never develop schizophrenia.
- *Acute phase.* Gradually or suddenly the positive symptoms, hallucinations and delusions, become apparent and take centre stage. For example, Damian's marks and behaviour had declined over a few months when, one evening, his father went looking for him to come and have dinner. He found Damian hiding under the bed with a sock in his mouth. 'The next-door neighbour is sucking my thoughts out through my mouth,' explained a terrified Damian.
- *Recovery stage.* With treatment, the symptoms gradually disappear after a period which varies from person to person. In many cases the recovery is not complete, leaving residual manifestations of the disease. This stage is then called the *residual phase.*

SPLIT MIND

Schizophrenia is a disease as old as humankind. However, it was not clearly separated from other mental disorders until the end of the nineteenth century when Emil Kraepelin, a German psychiatrist, described this illness in detail. He called it 'premature insanity' to denote its early onset. The word 'schizophrenia', which comes from the Greek and means 'split mind', was coined fifteen years later by Eugen Bleuler, a Swiss psychiatrist, to describe the tearing apart of the

---

> personality observed in this illness. People with schizophrenia do not have two, or several, different personalities or minds (this is a different disorder – multiple personality disorder – the existence of which is not widely accepted).
>
> Nevertheless, 'schizophrenia' is often used to mean two opposite or conflicting sides of a person or activity. For example, T. S. Eliot wrote, 'For a poet to be also a philosopher he would have to be virtually two men; I cannot think of any example of this thorough schizophrenia, nor can I see anything to be gained by it'.
>
> 'The use of poetry and the use of criticism', London, 1964, Faber & Faber 2nd edn, p. 98.

Schizophrenia is a relatively common condition that affects about 1 per cent of the population across the world. Both men and women are equally afflicted but men show the disturbance, on average, ten years earlier.

About one-third of the sufferers may recover completely after the first episode and lead a normal and productive life. Another third show exacerbations or recurrences of the acute phase and remissions, although even during the periods of remission some negative symptoms may persist. Some sufferers with recurrent episodes can keep a low-stress job, while some may have chronic and persistent symptoms that significantly incapacitate them for work.

About 60 per cent of individuals with this disorder never marry and have few social contacts. They tend to have lower-skilled jobs than their parents or siblings and often abuse alcohol or drugs. Depression, depressive feelings and inability to enjoy everyday activities and pastimes are also frequent. About one in ten, usually young males, will commit suicide. This is a serious and incapacitating condition.

Is there a way to know who will get well and who won't?

It is extremely difficult to predict during the first episode of the illness who will get well. Only the passage of time can answer this question. However, there are circumstances that are often associated with a good outcome. These are:

- The teenager was well adjusted prior to the beginning of the illness.
- The illness starts quite rapidly (as opposed to a very gradual decline over many months).
- The onset occurred after the age of 25 years.
- The teenager is female (overall women have a less severe illness).
- There were stressful life changes that preceded the onset of the disorder.
- The acute phase is short.
- There are few negative symptoms, such as lack of drive.
- There are almost no residual symptoms after the episode.

What causes schizophrenia?

Theories about schizophrenia are intertwined with the history of our perceptions of madness. Accordingly schizophrenia has been seen at various times as a sign of divine favour or a manifestation of damnation, as being caused by society's pressures and demands or as a physical illness of the brain. We still don't know for sure what specifically produces schizophrenia, but a few points are clear:

- It is an illness that affects the brain in some way, although we don't know the precise mechanism.
- It often runs in families.
- Some factors in the environment can trigger its onset or relapses.
- Stress, tension and conflict can cause a relapse in sufferers.
- It is unlikely that the way in which you treat your children will make them develop schizophrenia.

Recent advances in genetics, imaging and biochemistry will possibly produce clearer results in the near future.

What are the early signs of schizophrenia?

It is easy to see the early signs when looking back but it is difficult to notice the seriousness of them at the time. Most teenagers who develop schizophrenia show a personality change that becomes obvious after a while. They:

- are 'not the same'
- become more introverted
- are suspicious
- lose interest in friends and social activities
- spend much more time in their rooms
- lack former energy and drive
- lack interest in school work so that marks deteriorate
- become preoccupied by strange or bizarre ideas (e.g. people are against them, they have unusual powers, they begin to refuse some foods as if there was something wrong with them), which at this stage are not frank delusions and the teenager can often rationally explain them.

However, these changes are not exclusive to or even typical of schizophrenia. Because many teenagers who will never develop schizophrenia also lose interest in school and develop infatuations with music idols, UFOs and many other weird and wonderful things, no one can know for sure at this stage that something like schizophrenia is brewing.

> *It is easy to see the early signs of the illness when looking back but it is difficult to notice the seriousness of them at the time.*

If experts can't pick the illness at this stage, you can't blame yourself if you didn't notice the problem either. If a relative had schizophrenia you may be alerted to the problem, but it is very difficult to suspect anything like schizophrenia if there is no such history. The best thing to do is to keep an eye discreetly on your child and look for positive signs of the illness, chiefly hallucination or delusions.

Some of these teenagers, because they feel strange in ways they can't explain, unhappy and frustrated, turn to drugs such as marijuana to feel better. This can hasten the onset of florid psychotic symptoms such as 'voices' (auditory hallucinations) and delusions. If so, you should convince them to seek help and don't just explain this as a symptom of the drug use. It can be, but it may also be a psychotic illness.

What should I do if I suspect that my child has schizophrenia?

Because schizophrenia – or any other psychotic condition – is a serious medical illness, you should seek specialist help as soon as possible.

Starting treatment early can save many problems later and may improve the result. Therefore, don't delay treatment in the hope that problems will go away. It is much better to err on the side of caution by seeking a consultation to find out that there is nothing to worry about. If you feel that 'something is not right', even though you don't know exactly what, seek help.

Don't let prejudice, what people may think, or fear of your child being locked up in a psychiatric hospital get in the way of seeking help. Schizophrenia is an illness just like a physical illness. It is a sign neither of weakness nor of wickedness. Nowadays most people with a psychotic episode are treated as out-patients or by having professionals from a mental health team visit them regularly at home. If hospitalisation is required, most psychiatric wards are now part of

---

SCHIZOPHRENIA AND CREATIVITY

Rich and poor, wise and dull, black and white, anyone can suffer from this disease. Until not long ago some people believed there was an association between madness and creativity: that people could not be creative if they were not mad, at least a little. This is certainly not true of schizophrenia.

The legendary Russian ballet dancer Nijinsky, 'the god of ballet', became ill with schizophrenia at the age of 29 and could not perform again. During his short career at the beginning of the twentieth century, he had enthralled the world with his leaps and his sensitive and original interpretations of many ballet themes. Almost a hundred years earlier, Hölderlin, one of the most brilliant German lyric poets, also became ill with schizophrenia and was no longer productive. He had written two years earlier: 'For those who lend us the heavenly fire, the Gods, give us sacred sorrow too. Let it be so. A son of earth I seem; born to love and to suffer.'

---

acute general hospitals or private clinics. The time when people were institutionalised for life has long passed. If anything, people are discharged from hospital too soon these days.

What if your teenager thinks there is nothing wrong with him and refuses help? If this is a problem with many adolescents it is particularly so in those who suffer from a psychotic illness because they often *lack insight*. Their experiences are so real and they are so convinced they are true that they may think seeking treatment is part of a plot. They don't realise they have an illness. Sometimes they may even believe that their parents are not their parents but are part of the conspiracy.

Be patient but persistent. Try to follow the advice on seeking help in Chapter 4. On some occasions, if your child's behaviour has become very disturbed, an admission to hospital against his will might be required, as was described in Chapter 7.

Treatment of schizophrenia

Although there is not a cure, there are effective treatments to help schizophrenia sufferers recover from their illness and prevent relapse. With the appropriate treatment, most recover quickly. The first stage is a thorough assessment, as described in Chapter 4. This may include blood tests and X-rays to clarify the nature of the psychotic episode.

Treatment has two aspects: treatment of the acute phase and prevention of relapses. Medication is an essential part of the treatment. However, medication is not enough. The family needs education on how to manage the illness and the patient, while the sufferer also requires counselling and support.

The treatment setting

It is important to decide as soon as possible on the best setting for implementing treatment. The choice will depend largely on the circumstances and symptoms of the teenager and the family's ability to cope. These days most people with a psychotic episode are treated without hospitalisation. Professionals from a mental health team may visit them regularly at home to assess progress and monitor response to medication and side effects, and also to help the family.

Hospitalisation may be required when the young person is very disturbed or suicidal, or the family is unable to care for the patient. Some sufferers request admission to hospital so they can rest or feel safe. Hospitalisation has the advantage that symptoms and response to medication can be observed more closely. It also facilitates investigation, if required. On rare occasions an involuntary admission is required.

NEW (ATYPICAL) ANTIPSYCHOTIC MEDICATIONS	
Generic name	**Trade name**
Clozapine	Clopine®, Clozaril®
Olanzapine	Zyprexa®
Quetiapine	Seroquel®
Risperidone	Risperdal®

Drug treatment

The medications used in the treatment of schizophrenia are called *antipsychotic drugs*. They are effective not only in the treatment of schizophrenia but also in other psychological disorders.

The discovery of antipsychotic drugs (known as atypical or new antipsychotics) that are different from the drugs used during the last half century (the traditional antipsychotics) has produced a dramatic change in the treatment of schizophrenia. The new antipsychotic medications are as effective as the traditional ones and have fewer side effects. The more common are listed in the box above.

The traditional antipsychotics, such as chlorpromazine (Largactil®), fluphenazine (Modecate®), haloperidol (Serenace®, Haldol®), are used much less frequently now. They produce sedation, tiredness, and other short-term and long-term motor effects. These side effects are often unpleasant. The newer antipsychotics also have side effects. The most troubling for adolescents is weight gain, which can be considerable. Clozapine, one of the more effective atypical antipsychotic drugs, can have severe toxic effects in the blood and heart and those who take it must have regular tests. For this reason it is usually prescribed for people who do not benefit from other antipsychotic drugs.

Antipsychotic drugs are not addictive. They are usually taken orally once or twice daily. Some can be administered by injection and several can be given as an injection once or twice a month.

Family therapy

Family therapy aims to explain to parents and siblings the characteristics of the disorder, its treatment and how they can help the young person recover and prevent relapses. Practical support of carers is essential when the condition becomes chronic.

Individual psychotherapy

Psychotherapy aims to:
• help the teenager understand what is happening to him
• help the teenager come to terms with the illness and its treatment
• provide strategies to help sufferers to cope with or avoid stressful situations that may precipitate a relapse.

Intensive psychotherapy is usually ineffective and unnecessary. However, a trusting relationship with a psychiatrist who knows the teenager well and is able to see that teenager from time to time over a period of years is essential to identify early relapses and reduce impairments to a minimum. This continuity of care is difficult to achieve in community clinics because staff change often.

Rehabilitation

After a psychotic episode many teenagers find that they have missed schooling, lost friends and developed negative habits such as poor hygiene or getting up from bed late. They find themselves lonely or isolated and their ability to cope with their studies or work may not be what it used to be. They need rehabilitation, which may include things such as training in new work skills, learning how to budget, shop, cook, and so on.

My name is Julia. I am a schizophrenic. My illness began slowly, gradually, when I was between the ages of 15 and 17. During that time reality became distant, and I began to wander around in a sort of haze, foreshadowing the delusional world that was to come later. I also began to have visual hallucinations in which people changed into different characters, the change indicating to me their moral value. For example, the mother of a good friend always changed into a witch, and I believed this to be indicative of her evil nature.

Another type of visual hallucination I had at this time is exemplified by an occurrence during a family trip: the cliffs along the side of the road took on human appearance, and I perceived them as women, bedraggled and weeping.

At the time I didn't know what to make of these changes in my perceptions. On the one hand, I thought they came as a gift from God, but on the other hand, I feared that something was dreadfully wrong. However, I didn't tell anyone what was happening; I was afraid of being called insane. I also feared, perhaps incredibly, that someone would take it lightly and tell me nothing was wrong, that I was just having a rough adolescence, which was what I was telling myself. Anyway, I battled the illness alone until I was 21, at which point, having exhausted all reserves, I decided to leave college and see a psychiatrist.

After seeing the psychiatrist for a year, and at her suggestion, I returned to college on a part-time basis. Shortly after doing so, I was hospitalised for the first time. That hospitalisation marked the first time I ever admitted to anyone what was happening inside my head.

I had the feeling that I was dissolving and that pieces of me were going out into space; I feared that I would never be able to find them again. I was also very ashamed and thought that people were watching me. I was afraid of people to the extent that I wouldn't come out of my room when people were around. I ate my meals when my family was out or asleep. I thought that I must be in hell, and that part of the meaning of this particular hell was that no one else around understood that it was hell.

My second hospitalisation was one year later. There followed two other three-day hospitalisations, the first after being brought in by the police and the second a walk-in. By then, I was able to recognise when I was getting out of control. For quite some time I had been seeing 'space soldiers' on the streets who were watching me and who intended to kill me. Eventually I realised that I was losing my ability to function at all in reality, so a friend took me first to stay with her family and then, a couple of days later, when that wasn't enough, to the local mental health facility.

Finally I was given appropriate medication. With this medication I can stay in reality with minimal effort, and most of my delusions and hallucinations are now in the background. I still have days when reality is distant, but that is manageable.

A constant during most of these years under psychiatric care, and in the three years leading up to them, was the existence of an inner reality that was more real to me than the reality of the outside world. In this place I lived in underground caves, which were torture chambers of the gods who ruled there. The outer reality of these caves took the form of condemning auditory hallucinations. I heard voices telling me that all the torture was my fault, and that I was alien and didn't deserve to live in reality.

Something needs to be said about what hospitalisations meant to me. It was always a relief to finally end up in the hospital. By the time I got there, I had generally exhausted all reserves of normalcy, and it was a great relief to be around other people like me. It was a relief to be in a place where it did not matter if you went off somewhere in the middle of a conversation. It was a relief not to have to fight all the time to maintain a semblance of sanity. It was a relief to be where things that were real to me could be real. It was a relief to be able to be honest.

A note about being 'sane': medicine did not cause sanity, it only made it possible. Sanity came through a minute-by-minute choice of outer reality, which was often without meaning. Sanity meant choosing a reality that was not real to me, and having faith that one day the choice would be worth the fear involved and that one day it would hold meaning.

> I am now 34 years old. My life is relatively stable. In the early morning I deliver papers to local businesses, and later in the day I attend a day program for the mentally ill. In autumn I will return to college and study a course at a time. I am hoping it will work.
>
> Adapted from an anonymous account, published in *Schizophrenia Bulletin*, 1992, vol. 18, pp. 333–6.

Preventing relapse

Many young people do not recover completely or are at risk of having further relapses. Relapses can be very damaging because they produce more disruption to the sufferers' lives, work and families. While psychotic, some young people might act out their delusions (e.g. leave home because they believe they are being poisoned), be unable to cope at school or work, lose their job or accommodation. Some of this damage may be irreparable. A relapse often means that the process of treatment will need to start all over again. Therefore, preventing relapse is essential.

Preventing relapse is very important.

In most young people, relapse occurs because they stop taking the medication prematurely. While up to 60 per cent relapse when they cease taking medication, only 10 per cent relapse while on medication.

Living with schizophrenia

Living with a person who suffers from schizophrenia, apart from those young people who recover fully or almost fully, is hard. It requires much love, dedication, understanding and sacrifice. This book can't do justice to the difficulties you are likely to experience.

You will need to tap into all the resources available in the community. Joining groups of parents in similar circumstances is the best way to know what you should do, what resources are available (these change quickly and from place to place) and how to lobby the government for more and better services.

Alcohol, marijuana and other drugs

14

Most parents want to know that their children are not in danger from drugs and that they understand what drugs can do to them. This chapter deals with the prevention and detection of drug problems and ways of helping teenagers who start using drugs. Marijuana receives special attention because its use is becoming widespread among teenagers.

Human beings have been experimenting with substances that alter consciousness, energise, calm or relieve pain since time immemorial. The Bible, for example, describes how Noah planted a vineyard, 'and he drank of the wine, and became drunk, and lay uncovered in his tent' (Genesis 9:21). Psychoactive preparations are used in all cultures and controlled and moderate consumption of substances such as alcohol and coffee is an integral part of social interaction. It becomes a problem when people using drugs lose control of their consumption to the extent that it impairs their physical or mental health and interferes with their work, family life and social duties. The problem and its toll, in terms of both illness and suffering, does not require emphasising.

Drug use is particularly worrying during the teenage years, when experimentation with drugs and drug abuse typically starts. In spite of the magnitude of the problem, little is known about why drug consumption gets out of control in some cases and not in others. By the age of 15 almost all teenagers have used alcohol and 1–2 per cent already show signs of dangerous or harmful consumption.

> *If someone is going to become an addict, their alcohol or drug use starts during adolescence.*

Most parents want to know that their children are not in danger from drugs and that they understand what drugs can do to them. Parents often dread their children knowing about drugs, in the belief that if they know about them they may start using them. This is unrealistic: most teenagers come into contact with drugs very early and need to be prepared for this by sound knowledge.

Because alcohol and drug use are now widespread, some parents may underestimate the risks or become blasé about their children's consumption of alcohol or experimentation with drugs. Many parents of this generation of teenagers used drugs, particularly marijuana, when they were young and can find it difficult to set strict rules against drug use.

The risks of drug use go further than the psychological effects. They include motor vehicle accidents, injury due to fights (brawls between young men are very frequent in venues where alcohol is consumed), physical illnesses such as hepatitis and AIDS, as well as a variety of occupational problems (inability to perform at work).

Substance use may affect children in a variety of ways:

- during pregnancy, because of the effect on the unborn child of drugs consumed by the mother – although these effects are not well known yet they can be considerable (e.g. babies born addicted to heroin, 'crack' babies, foetal alcohol syndrome)
- when growing up, because of the influence on their upbringing of a parent who abuses substances (e.g. domestic violence, physical or sexual abuse, poverty)
- during adolescence, because of the direct effects of drug use (intoxication) or the drug-using lifestyle.

SOME CONCEPTS COMMONLY USED WHEN TALKING ABOUT DRUGS

- *Drug.* A drug is a substance that can alter psychological functions, mood or behaviour. These substances influence the mind (are psychoactive) in ways perceived as pleasant by the user. Some are legal but the use of the majority of them is illegal.
- *Drug intoxication.* This term is used to describe the psychological and physical manifestations of a drug ingested by an individual (e.g. alcohol intoxication can produce lack of concentration, disinhibition, aggressiveness and loss of memory). The subjective feeling of drug intoxication is often referred to as being 'high' or 'stoned'.
- *Drug abuse.* This is the repetitive use of a mind-altering substance that results in adverse consequences (e.g. missing school, a drop in marks), increased risks (e.g. of motor vehicle accidents, AIDS because of sharing needles), legal trouble (e.g. arrests) or family problems.
- *Tolerance.* This is a phenomenon that develops with repeated use: most people require increasing amounts of the drug to achieve the desired effect (feeling high).
- *Withdrawal.* When individuals have been using drugs for a while, they experience unpleasant feelings if they stop using them. Withdrawal symptoms (e.g. shakes, sweating, craving, feeling down) are different for each type of drug and can predominantly affect the body (e.g. nausea, fits in the case of alcohol and benzodiazepines) or the mind (e.g. craving for the drug). All drugs of abuse produce withdrawal symptoms of greater or lesser intensity after repeated use.
- *Addiction or dependence.* People are considered addicted (or drug-dependent) when they continue using the substance in spite of this creating problems or physical illness. Addicts have usually developed tolerance to the drug and suffer withdrawal symptoms if they cease using it.

A list of the more commonly used drugs and of the symptoms of intoxication for each group is included in the box below. In all cases, the severity of the symptoms is proportional to the amount ingested. Alcohol abuse causes the largest number of health and social problems; the other drugs still represent a small proportion of the overall problem. The importance of cannabis is gradually increasing as a result of complacency by adults and authorities, and the false perception that it is not harmful. In the United States, cocaine (more often as *crack* cocaine) is a very serious problem among some disadvantaged teenagers.

COMMON DRUGS OF ABUSE AND TYPICAL SYMPTOMS OF INTOXICATION

Type of drug	Symptoms of intoxication
Stimulants (amphetamines, methylphenidate, ecstasy, cocaine)	A feeling of 'high', euphoria, is followed by a sensation of increased strength or power, gregariousness and talkativeness. Disturbed heart rhythms (too fast or too slow) can also be observed; pupils are dilated. There is often increased perspiration, chills, nausea or vomiting, weight loss, restlessness or agitation and muscle weakness.
Cannabis (marijuana, hashish)	Intoxication typically starts with a 'high'. This is often followed by euphoria, increased sense of self-importance and laughter. Sedation, lethargy and difficulty carrying out complex tasks are common. Judgment is typically impaired and some users describe distorted sensory perceptions (e.g. sounds appear louder or different) and time seems to pass more slowly. Typically the eyes are red (bloodshot), the mouth dry, there is increased appetite and fast heartbeat.

Type of drug	Symptoms of intoxication
Hallucinogens (LSD, mescaline, some 'designer' drugs)	Intoxication initially produces restlessness, which is followed by feelings of euphoria (often alternating with anxiety or depression). There are changes in perceptions (e.g. sounds are 'seen'), illusions and, at higher amounts, hallucinations. Hallucinations are typically visual (e.g. geometric forms, persons or objects) and the user knows they are not real but induced by the drug. Dilatation of the pupils, palpitations, sweats and tremor are almost always present. Some users experience recurrences of the hallucinations while not under the effects of the drug (flashbacks).
Inhalants (glue, paint thinners, liquid paper)	Sniffing these substances produces apathy, aggressiveness and lack of judgment, or euphoria. Physical signs of intoxication include dizziness, lack of coordination and unsteady gait, seeing double or blurred vision, slurred speech, tremor, muscle weakness, drowsiness or even coma.
Opiates (morphine, heroin, codeine, methadone)	An initial euphoria and sense of well-being is followed by apathy, loss of interest in what is going on around, poor judgment and an unpleasant mood (dysphoria). Physical signs of intoxication include drowsiness (being 'on the nod') or even coma and death at high doses. Pupils are small, speech is slurred and attention and memory are impaired. Occasionally, they can produce hallucinations.
Alcohol, sedatives, hypnotics, anxiolytics: barbiturates, benzodiazepines (Valium®, Rohipnol® and many other antianxiety medications)	Slurred speech, lack of coordination, drowsiness (or even coma at large amounts), lack of concentration and judgment, and impairment of memory are typical.

Use of most drugs can result in a variety of other, less frequent problems. Some of them are associated with drug withdrawal. In the case of alcohol, withdrawal (delirium tremens) can be life-threatening, as it can be for other sedatives also. Habit-forming drugs frequently cause depressive symptoms, anxiety, panic, sexual dysfunction and trouble sleeping. Substance abuse markedly increases the risk of suicide (see Chapter 8). Almost all can cause a drug-induced psychosis (see Chapter 13).

A singularly Australian problem is the abuse of simple analgesics such as paracetamol or aspirin. These pain-relieving medications can be purchased over the counter, without a prescription (the sale of compound analgesics, such as Bex powder, was restricted years ago because they can produce kidney damage). It is not yet clear whether persistent use of simple analgesics can cause health problems in the long run. They are, however, very toxic on overdose.

Why do teenagers use alcohol or drugs?

Teenagers use drugs for the same reasons adults do – to have fun, to relax, to be part of a group, to cope with stress, boredom or pain. More often than not there are several reasons and these can change according to circumstances. Curiosity and the desire to fit into a group are very common reasons. Youngsters who have already begun to smoke cigarettes or use alcohol are at high risk of marijuana use.

> **Mental health problems increase the risk of alcohol and drug use.**

Mental health problems increase the risk of alcohol and drug use. For example, depressed adolescents are more likely to try marijuana, drink alcohol and smoke cigarettes. However, misuse and addiction rarely happen by accident. They usually appear in the context of personal problems and difficulties with the family or relationships.

Years of research have shown that teenagers who have a lot of spare money are more likely to use alcohol, tobacco and other drugs than teenagers who don't.

Who becomes an addict?

Some adolescents develop drug problems while most don't, despite having experimented with drugs. Those in the following groups are most at risk of drug abuse:

• Oppositional or rebellious teenagers who identify with anti-authority, anti-establishment groups in which drug use is condoned or encouraged.

• Socially insecure adolescents who have few friends and need to be accepted and to 'fit in' with a drug-using group.

• Young people whose parents or siblings drink alcohol to excess or use drugs such as marijuana.

• Teenagers with mental health problems (anxiety symptoms, depression, schizophrenia).

• Adolescents with conduct disorders.

• Teenagers who are worried about their sexual abilities – there is a myth among teenagers and many adults that drugs enhance sexual prowess. Adolescents are often preoccupied with sex and sexual performance; in these cases alcohol, opiates or marijuana may reduce anxiety and inhibitions when used in small amounts. However, frequent drug use decreases interest in sex and impairs performance.

DO I HAVE A DRINKING PROBLEM?

PLACE A MARK NEXT TO YOUR ANSWER:

• **How often do you have a drink containing alcohol?**

0 ☐ Never **1** ☐ Monthly or less **2** ☐ Once a week
3 ☐ 2–4 times a week **4** ☐ 5 or more times a week

• **How many standard drinks do you have on a typical day when you are drinking?** (A *standard drink* has 10 grams of alcohol and is equivalent to 1 glass of standard beer, 2 glasses of light beer, 1 glass of wine, or 1 nip of spirits.)

0 ☐ 1 drink **1** ☐ 2 drinks **2** ☐ 3 drinks
3 ☐ 4 drinks **4** ☐ 5 drinks

• **How often do you have six or more drinks on one occasion?**

0 ☐ Never **1** ☐ Less than monthly **2** ☐ Monthly
3 ☐ Weekly **4** ☐ Daily or almost daily

• **How often during the last year have you found that you were not able to stop drinking once you had started?**

0 ☐ Never **1** ☐ Less than monthly **2** ☐ Monthly
3 ☐ Weekly **4** ☐ Daily or almost daily

• **How often during the last year have you failed to do what was normally expected from you because of drinking?**

0 ☐ Never **1** ☐ Less than monthly **2** ☐ Monthly
3 ☐ Weekly **4** ☐ Daily or almost daily

• **How often during the last year have you needed a drink in the morning to get yourself going after a heavy drinking session?**

0 ☐ Never **1** ☐ Less than monthly **2** ☐ Monthly
3 ☐ Weekly **4** ☐ Daily or almost daily

• **How often during the last year have you had a feeling of guilt or remorse after drinking?**

0 ☐ Never 1 ☐ Less than monthly 2 ☐ Monthly
3 ☐ Weekly 4 ☐ Daily or almost daily

• **How often during the last year have you been unable to remember what happened the night before because you had been drinking?**

0 ☐ Never 1 ☐ Less than monthly 2 ☐ Monthly
3 ☐ Weekly 4 ☐ Daily or almost daily

• **Have you or someone else been injured as a result of your drinking?**

0 ☐ No 2 ☐ Yes, but not in the last year
4 ☐ Yes, during last year

• **Has a relative, a friend, a doctor or other health worker been concerned about your drinking or suggested you cut down?**

0 ☐ No 2 ☐ Yes, but not in the last year
4 ☐ Yes, during last year

ADD THE SCORES FOR ALL RESPONSES. SCORES ARE INTERPRETED AS FOLLOWS:

0	abstainer
1–6 (men), **1–5** (women)	non-hazardous drinking
7–12 (men), **6–12** (women)	hazardous or harmful alcohol use
13 +	alcohol dependence

Saunders J. B. et al. 1999, 'Development of the Alcohol Use Disorders Identification Test (AUDIT): WHO collaborative project on early detection of persons with harmful alcohol consumption', *Addiction* vol. 88, pp. 791–804.

Marijuana

Marijuana is the illegal drug most often used in Australia and internationally. Consumption of marijuana increased markedly during the last decade of the twentieth century. For example, in 1996 one in three Australian secondary school students had used cannabis at least once. Use increases rapidly with age from 7 per cent at 13 years of age to 41 per cent at 17 years of age. Surveys conducted in the 1970s and 1980s showed higher use among boys but by 2000 this difference had disappeared, suggesting that use among girls has increased at a quicker pace. The rates of marijuana use for other countries, for example in the United States, New Zealand and in Europe, are similar.

> **About half of all 17-year-olds have tried marijuana.**

Adolescence is the peak age to start using cannabis. Marijuana use today begins at a younger age and stronger forms of the drug are available. The younger people start using, the more likely they will progress to addiction. Up to one in ten of those who ever used marijuana may become dependent.

What is marijuana?

Marijuana is a mixture of the dried, shredded leaves, stems, seeds and flowers of the hemp plant (*Cannabis sativa*). Cannabis is a term that refers to marijuana and other drugs made from the same plant. Strong forms of cannabis include sinse-milla, hashish ('hash') and hash oil.

All forms of cannabis contain THC (delta-9-tetrahydro-cannabinol), the main active ingredient in marijuana. Marijuana's effect depends on the potency of the THC it contains and, because of selective breeding, strength has increased since the 1970s. Ordinary marijuana has an average of 3 per cent THC, sinse-milla (made from the buds and flowering tops of female plants) 8 per cent, and hash oil (a tar-like liquid distilled from hashish) as much as 43 per cent.

What happens after smoking marijuana?

The symptoms of intoxication have been described in the box on page 252. When marijuana is smoked, THC goes quickly into the blood and brain through the lungs. This can happen within a few minutes. When marijuana is eaten, THC is absorbed more slowly as it has to pass through the stomach. It can take up to one hour to experience the 'high' and effects can last up to twelve hours.

People feel intoxicated (high), have a dry mouth, rapid heartbeat, poor sense of balance and the eyes look red. As the immediate effects fade, usually after two to three hours, the user may become sleepy. Some users, especially people smoking it for the first time, may experience acute anxiety and have paranoid thoughts (a 'bad trip'). In rare cases, a user who has taken a very high dose can experience psychotic symptoms and may need emergency treatment. Other kinds of bad reactions can occur when marijuana is mixed with other drugs. THC stays in the body for several days after smoking. In heavy users, it can be detected weeks after they have stopped using marijuana.

Does smoking marijuana lead to using other drugs?

Teenagers start experimenting with the drugs that are easiest to get – tobacco, alcohol, pain killers and inhalants (glue, petrol, aerosol sprays and other products that are sniffed). Most teenagers who experiment with cannabis have already tried alcohol and tobacco. Anyone who doesn't smoke tobacco is much less likely to enjoy smoking substances such as cannabis.

However, most experts think that experimenting with drugs has little to do with the drug itself, apart from its availability. It has a lot to do with a teenager's propensity to take risks and break rules. Therefore, smoking marijuana is a warning which suggests that, for reasons unrelated to cannabis, your child is at risk of drug use.

Is marijuana harmful?

Cannabis can have immediate harmful effects and can cause damage to health over time. Marijuana interferes with memory for recent events and users may have trouble handling complicated tasks. For example, cannabis affects the abilities required for safe driving: alertness, concentration, coordination and the ability to react quickly. These effects can last up to twenty-four hours. Marijuana can also make it difficult to judge distances and react to signals and sounds on the road. Cannabis interferes with students' ability to learn and can diminish athletic performance. Drug users may become involved in risky sexual behaviour. There is a strong link between drug use, unsafe sex and the spread of HIV, the virus that causes AIDS.

What are the long-term effects of marijuana?

- *Cancer.* It is hard to find out whether marijuana alone causes cancer because many people who smoke marijuana also smoke cigarettes and use other drugs. Marijuana smoke contains similar cancer-causing compounds to tobacco, sometimes in higher concentrations.
- *Immune system.* Our immune system protects the body from infection. It is not certain whether marijuana damages the immune system. There is research showing that it impairs the ability of T-cells to fight off some infections. People with HIV and others whose immune system is impaired should not use marijuana.
- *Lungs.* People who smoke marijuana develop the same kinds of breathing problems that cigarette smokers have. They have a frequent cough, chronic bronchitis and more chest colds than non-smokers.
- *Pregnancy and breastfeeding.* Some studies have found that babies born to marijuana users were shorter, weighed less and had smaller head sizes than those born to mothers who did not use the drug. Smaller babies are more likely to develop health problems. When a nursing mother uses marijuana, some of the THC is passed to the

baby in her breast milk. THC in the mother's milk is much more concentrated than in the mother's blood.

- *Brain.* THC affects the nerve cells in the part of the brain where memories are formed. This makes it hard for the user to recall recent events and to learn while 'high'. Cannabis also causes a decrease in concentration and in sex drive.
- *Mind.* Some frequent, long-term marijuana users show lack of motivation. This includes not caring about what happens in their lives, having no desire to work regularly, suffering fatigue and a lack of concern about how they look. Marijuana use may trigger a psychotic breakdown in teenagers who are predisposed to the illness or a recurrence in people suffering from schizophrenia.

Can a person become addicted to marijuana?

Studies suggest that about one in ten teenagers who use marijuana show signs of addiction. That is, when they do not use the drug, they develop withdrawal symptoms such as restlessness, loss of appetite, trouble sleeping, weight loss and shaky hands.

Can marijuana be used as medicine?

There has been much argument recently about the possible medical uses of marijuana. In considering this, it is important to distinguish between whole marijuana and pure THC. Whole marijuana contains hundreds of chemicals. THC, made into a pill that is taken by mouth, may be useful for treating the nausea and vomiting that go with certain cancer treatments and to help AIDS patients eat more to keep up their weight.

Treatment of drug problems

Treatment of drug problems can be provided by general practitioners, mental health professionals (psychiatrists, psychologists) or specialist drug and alcohol services. Treatment of the various addictions is complex and cannot be covered here but some general information may be useful.

HARM REDUCTION VERSUS ABSTINENCE

Treatment approaches for drug abuse vary. Some aim to achieve abstinence while others aim at continuing drug use (e.g. controlled drinking) but try to minimise the harmful effects of the drug and of the drug-using lifestyle (the 'harm-reduction' approach).

Some countries, including Australia, have embraced a harm minimisation philosophy to many substance abuse problems. In others, such as the United States, the main orientation is towards achieving abstinence.

The harm reduction philosophy is based on the belief that substance use is a reality, that abstinence is unlikely in many cases, and that the key issue is to lessen the harmful effects of the drugs on the individual and the community. Examples of this philosophy are the supply of clean needles to addicts, medically supervised injecting rooms and methadone programs. The debate about what is best is ongoing and passionate. We are not close to the answer.

Treatment of substance abuse requires the user to be motivated to change. One of the main goals of treatment (and an important skill of the therapist) is to enhance what motivation there is so that it becomes stronger. This is often very difficult to achieve in adolescents. They usually believe that their drug use is not a problem ('I can stop if I want') and prefer partying and having a good time.

Detoxification, or withdrawal, is the first step in cases of addiction. This can usually be done at home but should be performed under medical supervision. Withdrawal is not the same for all drugs; each has its own symptoms and treatment. Some, such as cannabis, are more benign than others, such as sedatives.

Rapid opiate detoxification has become very popular among heroin addicts in recent years because it reduces the length and unpleasantness of heroin withdrawal. These procedures are not free from risk and evidence of their effectiveness is very limited. In these cases, detoxification is undertaken under general anaesthesia or sedation. Withdrawal is then induced by the administration of naltrexone (Revia®, an opiate antagonist). The procedure takes about one day.

Once substance use has ceased, preventing relapse becomes the priority. This may entail changes in friends and lifestyle. Membership of self-help groups, such as Alcoholics Anonymous (AA), is helpful for many people.

Can medication help?

There are medications that may reduce relapse in some drug users. In the case of alcohol, naltrexone (Revia®) in combination with counselling reduces the rate of relapse by lessening the enjoyment experienced when drinking alcohol. Another drug, acamprosate (Campral®), in combination with therapy reduces the craving and facilitates abstinence. Disulfiran (Antabuse®) is a drug that has been available for a long time. Individuals taking this medication experience severe discomfort if they drink alcohol. However, it can be dangerous and is only recommended in healthy persons who are very motivated to abstain. Naltrexone, which reduces the 'high', can also be helpful for motivated heroin-addicted persons after detoxification.

Many young people with a drug addiction also have other mental health problems, such as depression. Treatment of those conditions is important.

What can I do to help my child not abuse alcohol or drugs?

Prevention in this area is much more important than cure. Once habits of drug use are established, they are difficult to change. Most important is ensuring that your children grow up in an environment that supports self-esteem and healthy behaviour and suggestions about how to achieve this have been made throughout the book. Here are some suggestions that relate specifically to drugs and alcohol.

- Most important is to bring up your children in a climate in which legal drugs, such as alcohol, may be used in small amounts on special occasions and under your supervision, but their consumption is not encouraged. A family doesn't need to be teetotal but family members, particularly parents, should not abuse alcohol or become drunk.
- Make your children fully aware of the risks of experimenting with drugs.
- Delay as long as possible their beginning to smoke or drink. Young people often start at the bottom of the line by smoking cigarettes and then move on to using alcohol and marijuana, and finally graduate to 'hard' drugs. The later they start, the more mature they will be and the less likely to become 'hooked'.
- Teenagers, as a matter of principle, will push boundaries and test limits. If that is the case, their breaking rules and acts of bravado will include smoking cigarettes. If you allow them to smoke, this becomes part of the expected behaviour and they will then try something else, for example alcohol or marijuana.
- Make sure you know your children's friends and that they don't abuse alcohol or drugs.
- When your children attend parties, ensure there is adequate supervision.
- If your teenage child comes home intoxicated, it is a clear sign that something is not well. You need to take this seriously and not dismiss it as 'normal' adolescent mischief. Rather than groundings or punishments, it might be better to give the message that this is a health problem and organise an assessment or attendance at the appropriate drug education program or quit smoking program.
- If your child shows signs of emotional or behavioural problems, seek treatment for her as soon as possible.
- Don't give your children too much money and, as far as possible, don't give cash (e.g. give a telephone card rather than money to call home).
- Don't worry too much about what other parents or children do.

DRINK SAFELY: TIPS FOR YOUR TEENAGER

- Pace yourself.
- Sip, don't scull.
- Drink alternatives to alcohol (e.g. mineral water, tonic).
- Try not to mix drinks.
- Eat, but avoid salty foods.
- Drink lots of water.
- Stay clear of violent situations.
- Carry money for phone calls and cabs.
- Buy only small amounts of alcohol.
- Count your drinks.
- Try not to get caught in a shout.
- Dance.
- Take limited money.
- Try not to top up the glass.
- Drink light strengths of alcohol.
- Try not to stand at the bar.

Source: *Drink Drunk, the difference is U.*

Other problems

There are other mental health problems in adolescents. Describing each one in detail would make this book unwieldy and overwhelming. You will find in this chapter information about post-traumatic stress disorders, personality disorders, tics (Tourette's disorder) and bedwetting. All these conditions are important in their own way.

Post-traumatic stress

Incidents that are outside the range of usual human experience, typically involving personal injury or threatened death, such as an earthquake, war or extreme violence, can have lasting psychological effects in children and adolescents as well as adults. When this results in ongoing distress or impairment they are said to suffer from post-traumatic stress disorder.

Although not new, interest and knowledge about these conditions has flourished during the last twenty years. However, this is a very new field and there are still more questions than answers, particularly in the case of young people. This situation is further confused by litigation and claims for compensation, very often legitimate but also open to abuse.

STRESS, STRESSFUL SITUATIONS AND TRAUMATIC EVENTS

Any strain, interference or change that disturbs the normal functioning of a person can cause stress. Because living involves frequent change and a variety of challenging situations, stress is an inevitable part of life. To a large extent, well-functioning, successful individuals are those who are able to manage or control the effects of stressful situations.

There are three main types of stressful events or stresses. The most frequent are those that entail *change* and the severity of these stresses is usually related to the amount of change involved. A holiday would be a mildly stressful event; beginning high school, a promotion or a change of job would usually be moderately stressful; while migration would be a highly stressful event for most people.

Another common stress is the *loss* of loved ones through death or separation. The break-up of their parents' marriage, with the consequent loss of a parent, is a frequent and highly stressful event to which many young people are exposed these days. In this particular case, the loss is often compounded by having to move house, change school and experience a drop in living standards. These circumstances greatly increase the impact of the loss.

The third type of stress is represented by *threats* to the individual's life or safety. These are also called traumatic events. Only severely traumatic events, such as those that threaten death or serious injury (e.g. from military combat, violent personal assault, torture, earthquake, a severe motor vehicle accident or being diagnosed with a life-threatening illness) or threats to the physical integrity of another person (e.g. witnessing violent death or injury) are considered of enough severity to cause post-traumatic stress disorder.

Stress is not necessarily negative. Many people actually become more mature and stronger by dealing with and overcoming stressful (challenging) situations.

Stressful events are often associated with the onset of mental disorders, recurrences or relapses. Learning to cope and to manage stress is an important aspect of preventing mental health problems.

Post-traumatic stress disorder in adolescents produces similar manifestations to those seen in adults. Having been exposed to a severely traumatic event usually produces symptoms immediately: emotional numbness, detachment and lack of awareness of the surroundings. Afterwards, the incident is re-experienced again and again. Sometimes the person avoids situations that could bring memories of the tragedy and often there are other changes as well, such as irritability and difficulties concentrating.

> Alex, a teenage boy who saw his mother burn to death in a fire, became dazed, as if he were in a dream, and did not seem to realise that his life was also at risk when he was rescued by the fire-fighters. He had nightmares of fires, and images of his house burning popped into his head at any time during the day. He refused to go back to the street where he lived, and he became panicky and distressed when he saw a log fire at a relative's home. Alex's personality seemed to change after the fire. He lost interest in his previous hobbies, did not seem to enjoy things, his marks at school were not as good and he was startled even by a fly landing on his hand.

When symptoms appear shortly after the traumatic event the condition is called *acute stress disorder*. The term *post-traumatic stress disorder* is reserved for people in whom manifestations persist (or begin) one month after the event.

These conditions are more frequent in adolescents who are vulnerable, either because of their personality (e.g. they are fearful and shy) or because they lack support (e.g. they have a poor relationship with their parents and no friends). When the traumatic event is extreme, anyone is likely to develop this disorder. Symptoms disappear within three months in about 50 per cent of the cases. However, most adolescents exposed to traumatic events who show any of the symptoms mentioned above are likely to benefit from counselling.

Disorders of the personality

Personality is the way in which we think of ourselves, perceive other people and relate to them. Personality is something enduring that distinguishes each one of us through life. People talk about personality characteristics when they say things such as 'He is reliable', 'She is a very disorganised person', 'He likes drama and showing off', 'She is very tidy', 'He is suspicious and trusts nobody'.

A personality disorder is present when these traits become so rigid and intense that they interfere with that person's ability to function normally. For example, John is a very tidy and organised teenager. He seldom allows his room to become messy and tidies his desk when he finishes work. He is methodical in his work habits and seldom leaves something for tomorrow. Because he is so organised he finds time for almost everything. He gets top marks at school and has time for sports and to go to the movies with his girlfriend. Clearly, these characteristics of John's personality are positive, they allow him to be successful and make his parents the envy of all the parents in the street.

By contrast, let's look at Adrian. His room and desk are tidy but he spends an enormous amount of time tidying them up. He wants to do his assignments so well that this actually prevents him from handing them in on time. He can't make up his mind about going to the movies or the football, so much so that when he finally decides to go it is often too late. Adrian is well known for arriving late everywhere because of the time he takes to get ready. His routine is rigid and he continuously worries about little details. He holds onto things forever 'just in case' they might be useful, with the result that he has drawers full of junk, which irritates his parents no end. Adrian, who is as intelligent as John, is not successful because he is impaired by his fastidiousness. He does not have many friends because people become tired and frustrated with him. If Adrian had always been like that he would be said to have a personality disorder.

Differences between the common mental disorders and personality disorders are important but difficult to describe. Most mental disorders are episodic, that is, they usually have a starting point and an end point. They happen to the individual and influence the individual's personality while present. However, once the disorder is treated, that individual's personality usually returns to the way it was. The effect on an adolescent is the same as that of a physical illness, such as a bad bout of influenza. While ill, he may need to be in bed, won't be able to concentrate on work and may be emotional or irritable. Once the influenza is over, however, he becomes his normal self again. Personality disorders, on the other hand, are different: the personality itself is abnormal, all the time.

Disorders of the personality are characterised by dysfunctional patterns of behaviour that persist through most of adult life. These patterns are rigid and not appropriate to the situations. They can be seen in persons who are suspicious all the time and can't trust others, or those who are so afraid of being rejected that they are prevented from making friends or developing relationships. These disorders often make people feel unhappy and interfere with work and relationships. In many instances, however, people with personality disorders don't seem to be aware that their behaviour is very objectionable and don't care how this affects other people. The most obvious example of this is antisocial personality disorder, which was described in Chapter 11.

Because personality is being formed during childhood and adolescence, personality disorders are not usually diagnosed until after the age of 18 years, although many are apparent well before then.

Personality disorders affect about 10 per cent of the adult population. When present, they complicate other disorders, such as depression and anxiety, and make their treatment much more difficult.

There are three groups of personality disorders:

- The first consists of individuals who are odd and eccentric. They are often loners who enjoy their own company and don't trust other people. They may have strange beliefs and interests.
- The second group comprises persons who are emotional and dramatic. They often break rules, are emotionally shallow and

BORDERLINE PERSONALITY DISORDER

Borderline personality disorder is often observed in older adolescents who create a lot of anxiety for relatives, helping agencies and therapists. People with this disorder are characterised by a marked instability in all areas of their life:

- They are afraid of being abandoned because they can't tolerate being alone. Their frantic efforts to avoid what they perceive as abandonment and elicit care lead them to perform dramatic, impulsive acts such as self-mutilation or attempted suicide.
- Their relationships are intense and unstable. They idealise other people very quickly, but devalue them as rapidly because they feel the other person does not care enough or is not there enough for them.
- Their self-image, career goals, values, sexual identity and type of friends can change suddenly and dramatically.
- They are impulsive and self-destructive: they gamble, binge-eat, spend money irresponsibly, engage in unsafe sex or drive recklessly. They often abuse alcohol or drugs.
- Their mood changes rapidly from depression to happiness, from fear to anger. Fits of temper and physical fights are frequent.
- They have chronic feelings of emptiness and boredom.

This condition afflicts 2 per cent of the population, 75 per cent of whom are female. It is more common if relatives have the condition and is often associated with severe emotional deprivation during infancy. Women who have been the victims of incest are over-represented among those with borderline personality. Borderline personality is frequent among teenagers with bulimia and with drug and alcohol problems. A substantial number commit suicide.

Treatment, which is difficult, is mainly with individual psychotherapy. Admission to hospital might be required, but usually for very short periods in times of crisis. Lengthy admissions typically worsen the symptoms.

self-centred, like to be the centre of attention all the time and use other people for their own ends. They often feel entitled to special treatment and have an inflated sense of their own self-importance. Antisocial personality disorder is one example of these disorders, another is borderline personality disorder (see the box on page 271).

• The third group of personality disorders includes fearful and anxious individuals. They are insecure, worry too much about being criticised or rejected and have low self-esteem. They often lack assertiveness and are too preoccupied with details.

The treatment of personality disorders is difficult, takes time and requires motivation to change. Treatment is mainly through individual psychotherapy or counselling.

Tourette's disorder

Tourette's disorder is a chronic condition characterised by motor and vocal tics that wax and wane in severity and are often accompanied by a variety of behavioural problems, including ADHD (see Chapter 11) and some forms of obsessive compulsive disorder (see Chapter 9).

TICS

Tics are sudden, rapid, repetitive and stereotyped movements or vocal sounds. They seem purposeful but are, in fact, purposeless. They can be:

• simple, such as eye blinking or clearing the throat
• complex, such as tidying the hair with the hand or jumping,
• motor, such as shrugging the shoulders or smelling an object
• vocal, such as throat clearing, repeating words (often obscene – coprolalia) or phrases out of context.

The teenager experiences the tic as irresistible but usually can suppress it for a short period of time. Tics become worse when the teenager is under stress, diminish when he is doing something pleasant or absorbing, and disappear during sleep.

In people with this condition, motor tics start at about 7 years of age as transient bouts of tics affecting the eyes, face or head. Vocal tics (noises, swearwords) typically begin at about 11 years. They are at their worst during early adolescence and improve thereafter. Symptoms wax and wane and the type of tic may change from time to time. About 60 per cent of these people show obsessive compulsive behaviours, mainly touching, tapping and rubbing.

This is a condition that has attracted much research interest in recent years because it bridges the gap between disorders of the brain and those of the mind. It should only be treated in moderate or severe cases that produce impairment. Severe forms can be very handicapping. Treatment is with medication; some antipsychotic drugs, such as haloperidol (see Chapter 13), are effective although this is not a psychotic illness. Other medications, such as clonidine (see Chapter 11), are useful also.

You should suspect the possibility of Tourette's disorder if your child starts blinking often, makes other repetitive movements ('habits' such as grimacing or jerky movements of the head) and subsequently begins to make frequent noises (throat clearing, grunting, sniffing, snorting). Swearing, when present, is quite puzzling (it may be difficult to distinguish this as a symptom of Tourette's disorder from 'normal' adolescent conduct). If you are concerned about the possibility that your child might have this problem, request a referral to a paediatrician, psychiatrist or neurologist.

Bedwetting

Nocturnal enuresis is an old human scourge mentioned in the Ebers papyrus, an Egyptian compilation of medical texts dated 1550 BC. This is a common problem that affects about 1 per cent of adults and 5 per cent of 10-year-olds.

No single factor has been identified as directly causing enuresis. However, it is much more frequent in boys and people with a family history of bedwetting. Contrary to what was previously believed, bedwetting is not the result of emotional problems or mental disorders. If teenagers have emotional problems these don't usually cause their wetting the bed, although bedwetting gets worse or can resume when they are under stress. If anything, bedwetting may cause low self-esteem because the young person may feel embarrassed, is unwilling to sleep over at friends' places or go to camps. This deceptively simple and apparently banal problem can reduce the quality of life of sufferers and their families considerably.

Conditioning devices ('bell and pad') are the most effective treatment. These consist of a rubber pad that is placed under the bed sheet and on top of the mattress. When the pad becomes wet it switches on a bell that wakes the teenager up. The adolescent is then supposed to get up and change the wet sheets for dry ones. About 80 per cent of sufferers overcome this problem after two or three months of consistent use. The bell and pad device can be purchased in many pharmacies or borrowed from child health services. However, drugs are the preferred treatment of both physicians and families. The traditional antidepressants, particularly imipramine, are effective but have significant risks and unwanted effects (see Chapter 6). In most cases bedwetting resumes as soon as the child stops taking the medication.

There is always hope

You may recall from Chapter 5 the case of a man in his forties who had been afflicted by bedwetting all his life and who had not obtained relief from any treatment. He finally found an effective remedy: desmopressin, a synthetic hormone that reduces urine production. He took some each night and was finally able to sleep in a dry bed.

If you persist, there is always hope. Even the most difficult problems can be overcome, let alone small ones.

Appendix A

Some other resources that can be of help

General books on normal development

American Academy of Child & Adolescent Psychiatry, *My Adolescent*, HarperCollins: New York, 1999.

A comprehensive description of teenage development and its problems.

Bennett, D., *Growing Pains*, Doubleday: Sydney, 1995.

What to do when your children become teenagers.

Cooke, K., *Real Gorgeous: The Truth About Body and Beauty*, Allen & Unwin: Sydney, 1997.

On what is 'normal' in the world of the body, health and beauty.

Irwine, J., *Thriving at School*, Simon & Schuster: Sydney, 2000.

A practical guide to help your child enjoy the crucial school years.

Rutter, M. and Rutter, M., *Developing Minds*, Penguin: London, 1992.

An excellent, erudite description of psychological development.

General books on mental disorders

Bloch, S. and Singh, B.S., *Understanding Troubled Minds: a Guide to Mental Illness and its Treatment*, Melbourne University Press: Melbourne, 1997.

Kosky, R.J., Eshkevari, H.S. and Carr, V.J., *Mental Health and Illness: A Textbook for Students of Health Sciences*, Butterworth-Heinemann: Sydney, 1991.

Sawyer, M.G. et al., *The Mental Health of Young People in Australia: Child and Adolescent, Component of the National Survey of Mental Health and Wellbeing*, Australian Government Publishing Service: Canberra, 2000.

This booklet presents the findings of a survey that gives reliable information on the burden of mental illness in children and adolescents in Australia.
Free copy of the report is available online at
http://www.health.gov.au/hsdd/mentalhe/resources/young/index.htm

Surgeon General's Report on Children's Mental Health.

This excellent publication prepared by the Surgeon General of the United States of America can be obtained free online at
http://www.surgeongeneral.gov/cmh/default.htm

Booklets specifically written for young people with emotional problems

National Health and Medical Research Council, *Getting up From Feeling Down: Young People and Depression*, Australian Government Publishing Service: Canberra, 1997.

National Health and Medical Research Council, *Blue Daze: A Comic Book for Young People*, Australian Government Publishing Service: Canberra, 1997.

Free copies of *Getting up From Feeling Down* and *Blue Daze* are available by calling 1800- 020 103 or online at
http://www.health.gov.au/nhmrc/publications/synopses/cp37to41.htm

Wever, C. and Phillips, N., *The Secret Problem*, Shrink-Rap Press: Sydney, 1994.
A booklet for young people with obsessive compulsive disorder.

Wever, C. and Phillips, N., *The School Wobblies*, Shrink-Rap Press: Sydney, 1994.
For young people who find it hard to go to school.

Wever, C. and Phillips, N., *Full of Beans*, Shrink-Rap Press: Sydney, 1998.
For children and young adolescents with Attention Deficit Hyperactivity Disorder.

These three booklets can be purchased by writing to PO Box 187 Concord West NSW 2138, Australia, fax: 02- 9743 5936, email: shrap@geko.net.au

Books on specific problems

Ball, J., Butow, P. and Place, F., *When Eating is Everything*, Jillian Ball and Fiona Place: Sydney, 1997.

On eating disorders.

Green, C. and Chee, K., *Understanding ADD. Attention Deficit Disorder*, Doubleday: Sydney, 1997.

Kelly, M., *Life on a Roller Coaster: Living Well with Depression and Manic Depression*, Simon & Schuster: Sydney, 2000.

National Health and Medical Research Council, *Learning Difficulties in Children and Adolescents*, Australian Government Publishing Service: Canberra, 1990.

A booklet prepared by the Expert Advisory Panel on Learning Difficulties in Children and Adolescents. It describes the causes, assessment and treatment in a clear and concise manner.

Rapee, R.M., Spence, S.H., Cobham, V. and Wignall, A.M., *Helping Your Anxious Child: A Step-by-Step Guide for Parents*, New Harbinger Publications, Inc: Oakland, CA, USA, 2000.

Practical suggestions for parents to help young people with separation anxiety problems and other anxiety disorders.

Rapoport, J., *The Boy who Couldn't Stop Washing: The Experience and Treatment of Obsessive Compulsive Disorder*, Collins: London, 1990.

Good description of obsessive compulsive disorder including patients' accounts as well as advice about diagnosis and treatment.

Schou, M., *Lithium Treatment of Manic-Depressive Illness: A Practical Guide*, S. Karger AG: Basel, Switzerland, 1989.

A booklet that describes in detail all the matters about lithium treatment that may be of interest to sufferers or their relatives.

Serfontein, G., *The Hidden Handicap*, Simon & Schuster: Sydney, 1990.

A popular book about children with ADD and learning problems.

Internet resources

There is an enormous wealth of information on the Internet. However, much of that information is incorrect or even misleading. Sometimes it is difficult to assess its quality, particularly by people who do not have specialised knowledge in the area. I list here some reliable sites that provide high-quality, up-to-date information for parents, adolescents and professionals.

Sites that provide general mental health information

American Psychiatric Association
http://www.psych.org

American Psychological Association
www.apa.org

American Academy of Child & Adolescent Psychiatry
http://www.aacap.org/

AusEinet - Australian Early Intervention Network for Mental Health in Young People
http://auseinet.flinders.edu.au

Center for Mental Health Services (USA)
http://www.mentalhealth.org/

Mental Health Council of Australia
http://www.mhca.com.au/

Mental health information for consumers, carers and families

Commonwealth of Australia, Department of Health and Aged Care
http://www.health.gov.au/hsdd/mentalhe/mhinfo/ccf/index.htm

MindMatters (Australia)
http://www.curriculum.edu.au/mindmatters

National Institute of Mental Health (USA)
http://www.nimh.nih.gov/publicat/index.cfm

National Mental Health Association (USA)
http://www.nmha.org/index.cfm

NSW Multicultural Health Communication Service: quality information about health issues and health services to people of non-English speaking backgrounds (Australia)
http://www.mhcs.health.nsw.gov.au/

Psych-Net Mental Health (USA)
http://psych-net.org

The Mental Health Foundation of New Zealand
http://www.mentalhealth.org.nz

The Royal Australian and New Zealand College of Psychiatrists
http://www.ranzcp.org/

Consumer and carer organisations

Australian Drug Foundation
An independent, non-profit organisation working to prevent and reduce alcohol and drug problems in the Australian community
www.adf.org.au

Children and Adults with Attention Deficit Disorder (USA) www.chadd.org

Families Worldwide (USA)
www.fww.org

Family Drug Support
A site designed to assist families to deal with drug issues (Australia)
www.fds.org.au

Federation of Families for Children's Mental Health (USA) www.ffcmh.org

National Alliance for the Mentally Ill (USA)
www.nami.org

SANE Australia
http://www.sane.org

Drug and alcohol problems

Canadian Centre on Substance Abuse maintains one of the best
up-to-date sets of key links
www.ccsa.ca/

Center for Education and Information on Drugs and Alcohol
(CEIDA)(Australia)
http://www.ceida.net.au/

Center for Treatment Research on Adolescent Drug Abuse (USA)
www.med.miami.edu/ctrada

NSW Government. Office of Drug Policy website
www.druginfo.nsw.gov.au

Sites with information about specific problems

Child and Adolescent Bipolar Foundation (USA)
www.cabf.org

Commission for the Prevention of Youth Violence (USA)
www.ama-assn.org/ama/pub/category/3536.html
Madison Institute of Medicine - information on lithium, bipolar disorder
treatment and obsessive compulsive disorders (USA)
www.miminc.org

National depression initiative: Beyond Blue (Australia)
http://www.beyondblue.org.au

The Center for the Study and Prevention of Violence (USA)
www.colorado.edu/cspv/infohouse/factsheets.html

The Early Psychosis Prevention and Intervention Centre (EPPIC) (Australia)
http://home.vicnet.net.au/%7Eeppic/

Suicide prevention

Australian Institute for Suicide Research and Prevention
http://www.gu.edu.au/school/psy/aisrap

Australian Institute of Family Studies – National Youth Suicide Prevention
Communication Project
http://www.aifs.org.au/ysp

National Youth Suicide Prevention Strategy, Resource Guide on Education and
Training (Australia)
http://www.ysp.medeserv.com.au

Suicide Prevention Information New Zealand
http://www.spinz.org.nz

Appendix B

Where to seek help

In case of crisis you or your child may contact:

Lifeline, phone: 13 11 14

http://www.lifeline.org.au/

Kids Help Line, phone: 1800 551 800

http://www.kidshelp.com.au/

Services and agencies change rapidly, what is available one month may not be available the next. The best way to find out what services are available is by asking your family doctor, paediatrician or school counsellor.

ReachOut is an Australian Internet site specifically designed to help young people with mental health problems. Up-to-date information about resources is also available for the families of young people in need and the professionals who work with them. http://www.reachout.asn.au/

If you need further details, you should ask your local community health centre or community mental health centre for more infor-mation. You will find their phone numbers listed in the telephone directory. If this fails, you may telephone the local adolescent service, if there is one, the child and adolescent department of the local children's hospital or your local hospital.

There are many support groups for parents and sufferers. It is impossible to list them all here. For example, there are attention deficit disorder support groups in most capital cities. Look in the telephone book under the heading Attention Deficit Disorder, ADD or ADHD. Some of the Internet addresses of support groups can be found in the section on Internet resources, Appendix A.

The Mental Health Association in your state or territory (look under 'Mental Health' in the telephone directory) will provide you with the names and addresses of these support groups. The mental health section of the Department of Health in your state or territory will also be able to point you in the right direction.

Index